MESSAGES
FROM YOUR
Angels
COLOURING BOOK

MESSAGES
FROM YOUR
Angels
COLOURING BOOK

DOREEN VIRTUE

Illustrations by Norma J. Burnell

HAY HOUSE

Carlsbad, California • New York City • London • Sydney
Johannesburg • Vancouver • Hong Kong • New Delhi

First published and distributed in the United Kingdom by:
Hay House UK Ltd, Astley House, 33 Notting Hill Gate, London W11 3JQ
Tel: +44 (0)20 3675 2450; Fax: +44 (0)20 3675 2451; www.hayhouse.co.uk

Published and distributed in the United States of America by:
Hay House Inc., PO Box 5100, Carlsbad, CA 92018-5100
Tel: (1) 760 431 7695 or (800) 654 5126
Fax: (1) 760 431 6948 or (800) 650 5115; www.hayhouse.com

Published and distributed in Australia by:
Hay House Australia Ltd, 18/36 Ralph St, Alexandria NSW 2015
Tel: (61) 2 9669 4299; Fax: (61) 2 9669 4144; www.hayhouse.com.au

Published and distributed in the Republic of South Africa by:
Hay House SA (Pty) Ltd, PO Box 990, Witkoppen 2068
info@hayhouse.co.za; www.hayhouse.co.za

Published and distributed in India by:
Hay House Publishers India, Muskaan Complex, Plot No.3, B-2,
Vasant Kunj, New Delhi 110 070
Tel: (91) 11 4176 1620; Fax: (91) 11 4176 1630; www.hayhouse.co.in

Distributed in Canada by:
Raincoast Books, 2440 Viking Way, Richmond, B.C. V6V 1N2
Tel: (1) 604 448 7100; Fax: (1) 604 270 7161; www.raincoast.com

A catalogue record for this book is available from the British Library.

ISBN: 978-1-78180-745-3

Printed and bound by CPI Group (UK) Ltd, Croydon, CR0 4YY

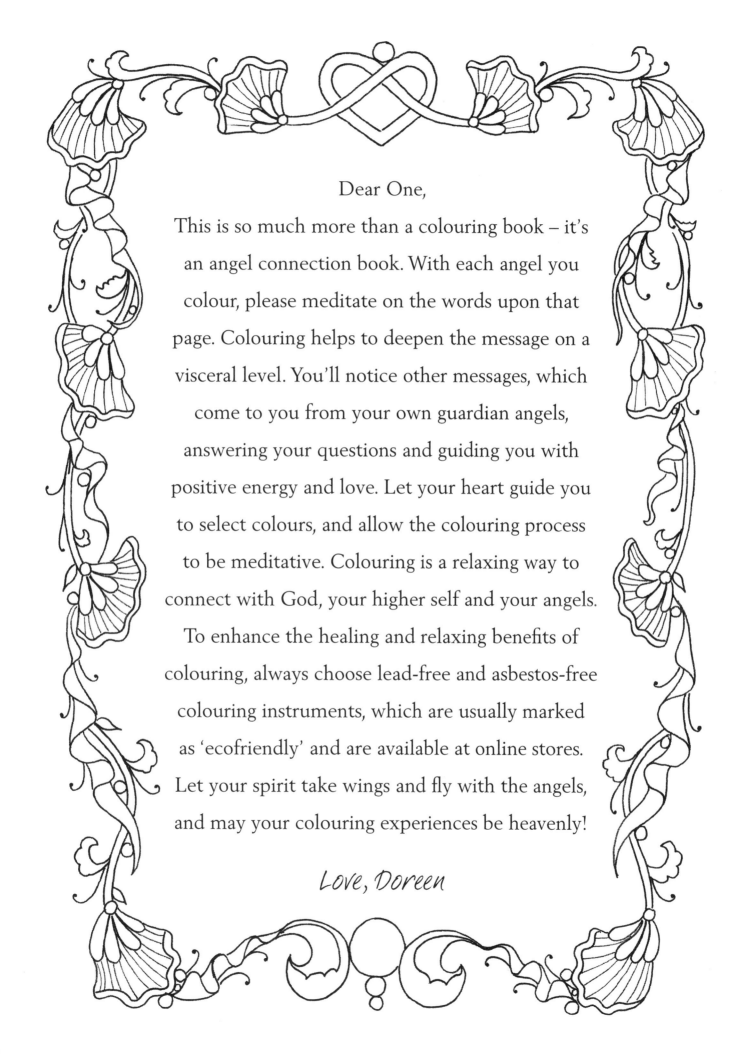

Dear One,

This is so much more than a colouring book – it's an angel connection book. With each angel you colour, please meditate on the words upon that page. Colouring helps to deepen the message on a visceral level. You'll notice other messages, which come to you from your own guardian angels, answering your questions and guiding you with positive energy and love. Let your heart guide you to select colours, and allow the colouring process to be meditative. Colouring is a relaxing way to connect with God, your higher self and your angels. To enhance the healing and relaxing benefits of colouring, always choose lead-free and asbestos-free colouring instruments, which are usually marked as 'ecofriendly' and are available at online stores. Let your spirit take wings and fly with the angels, and may your colouring experiences be heavenly!

Love, Doreen

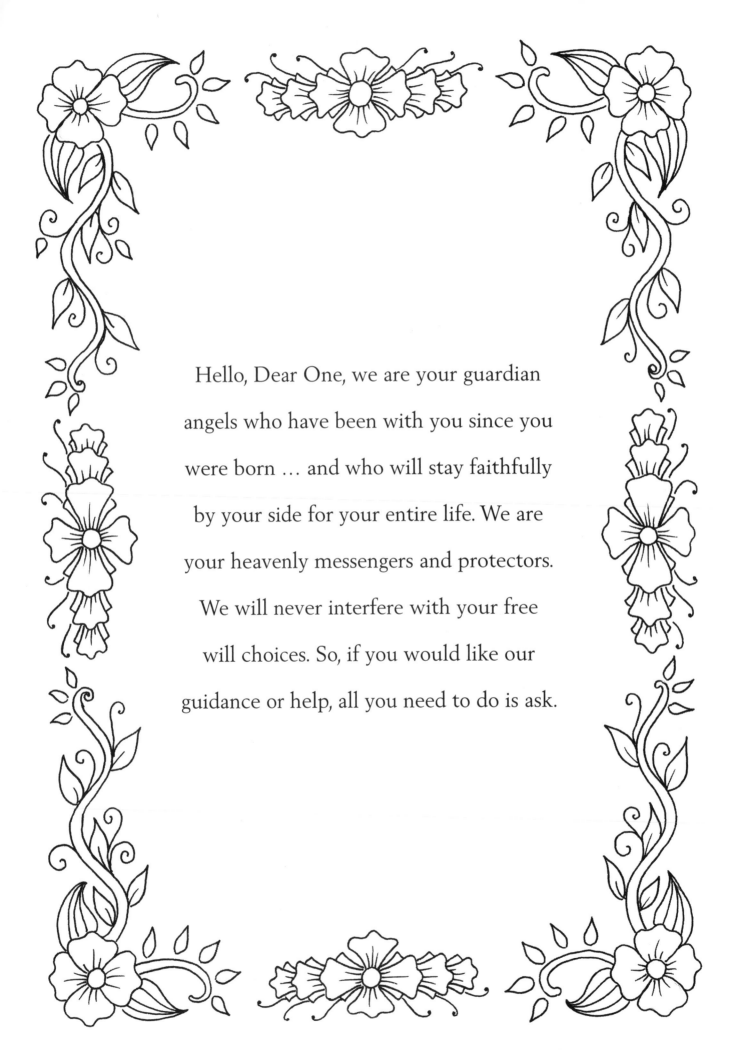

Hello, Dear One, we are your guardian angels who have been with you since you were born … and who will stay faithfully by your side for your entire life. We are your heavenly messengers and protectors. We will never interfere with your free will choices. So, if you would like our guidance or help, all you need to do is ask.

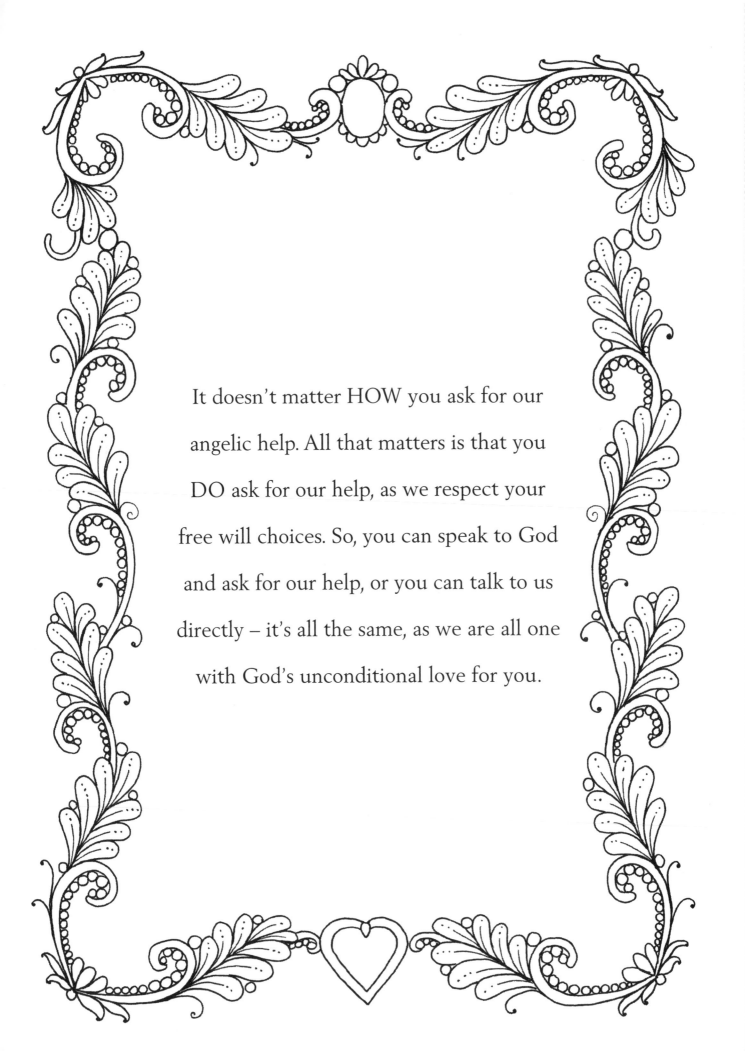

It doesn't matter HOW you ask for our angelic help. All that matters is that you DO ask for our help, as we respect your free will choices. So, you can speak to God and ask for our help, or you can talk to us directly – it's all the same, as we are all one with God's unconditional love for you.

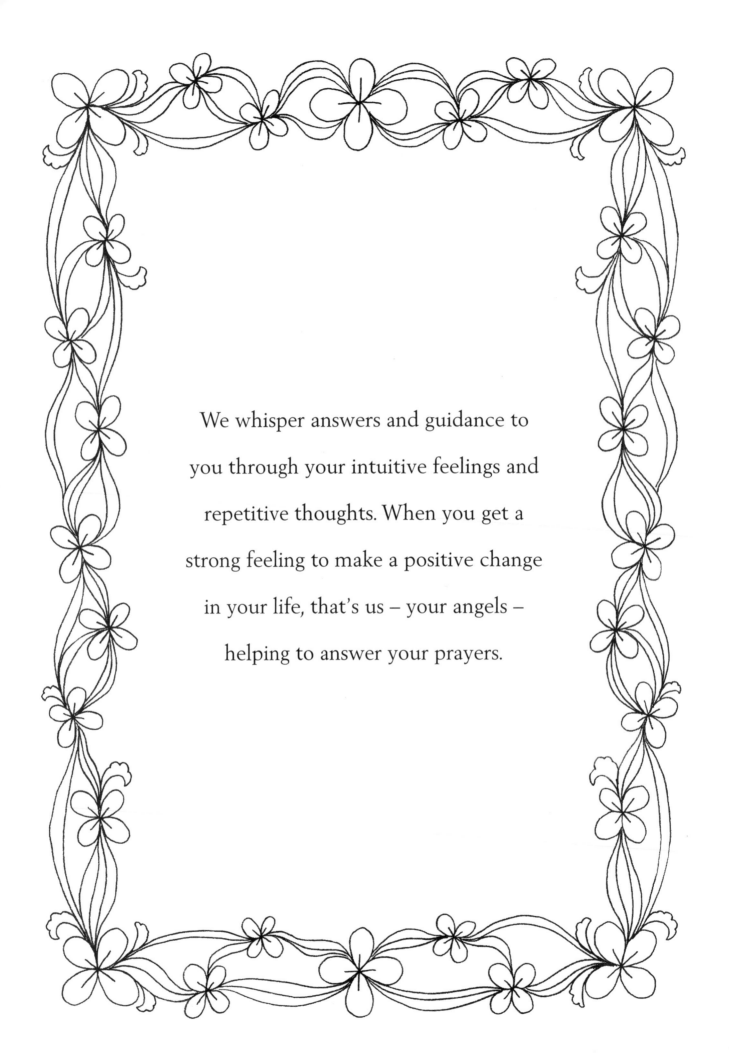

We whisper answers and guidance to
you through your intuitive feelings and
repetitive thoughts. When you get a
strong feeling to make a positive change
in your life, that's us – your angels –
helping to answer your prayers.

We also send you signs from above, such as feathers, coins, rainbows, songs, birds and butterflies. When you see or hear a sign, and you have a strong feeling that it's a message from heaven … trust that feeling, because you're right! Don't worry that you'd miss receiving a sign, because we send them to you repeatedly so that you'll know they are beyond coincidence.

We know that sometimes you feel lonely
or misunderstood by other people, and
that's when we gather even closer to your
side. Please know that we angels love you
unconditionally, and we can see your inner
goodness and beauty. We are your eternal
friends whom you can call upon at any time.

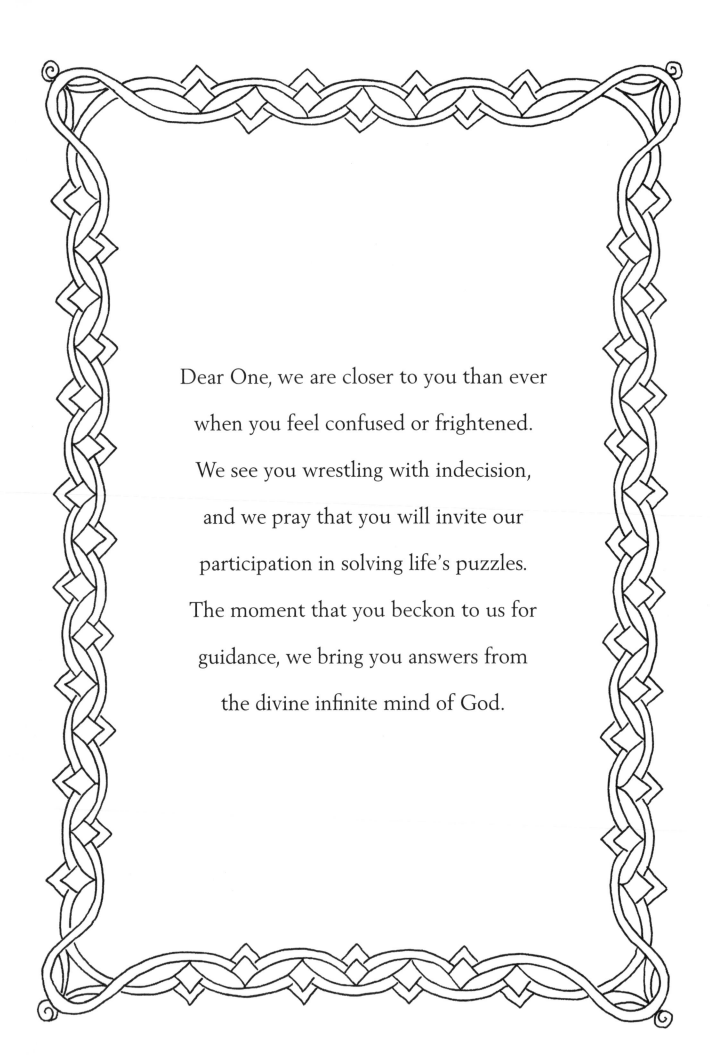

Dear One, we are closer to you than ever

when you feel confused or frightened.

We see you wrestling with indecision,

and we pray that you will invite our

participation in solving life's puzzles.

The moment that you beckon to us for

guidance, we bring you answers from

the divine infinite mind of God.

You can hear us through your strong

feelings, which are the stirrings to take

positive actions to improve your life and the

lives of others. We send you these signals

through your emotional, physical and

intuitive feelings. If you need help

in interpreting the feelings, just ask,

and we will send you signs and clarity.

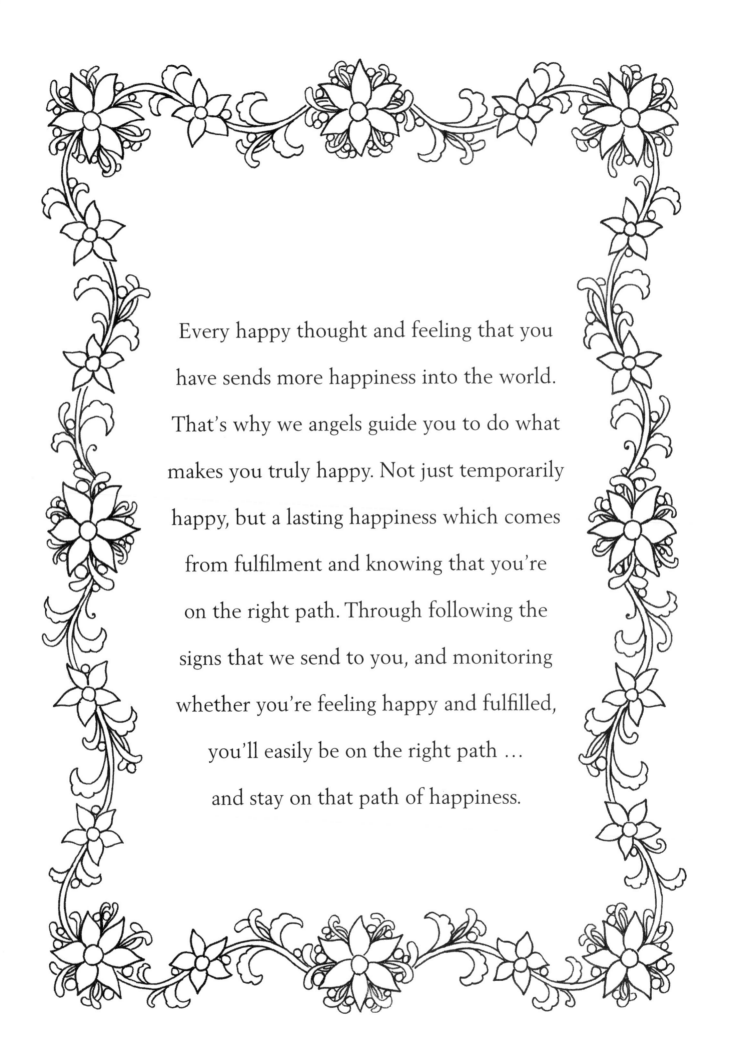

Every happy thought and feeling that you
have sends more happiness into the world.
That's why we angels guide you to do what
makes you truly happy. Not just temporarily
happy, but a lasting happiness which comes
from fulfilment and knowing that you're
on the right path. Through following the
signs that we send to you, and monitoring
whether you're feeling happy and fulfilled,
you'll easily be on the right path …
and stay on that path of happiness.

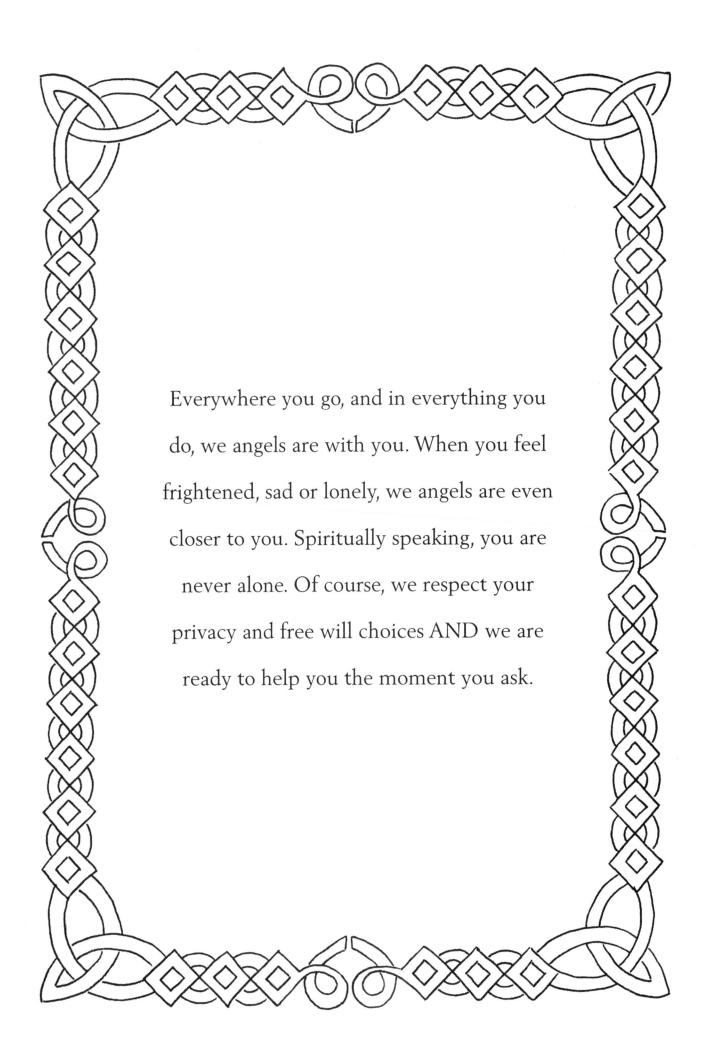

Everywhere you go, and in everything you do, we angels are with you. When you feel frightened, sad or lonely, we angels are even closer to you. Spiritually speaking, you are never alone. Of course, we respect your privacy and free will choices AND we are ready to help you the moment you ask.

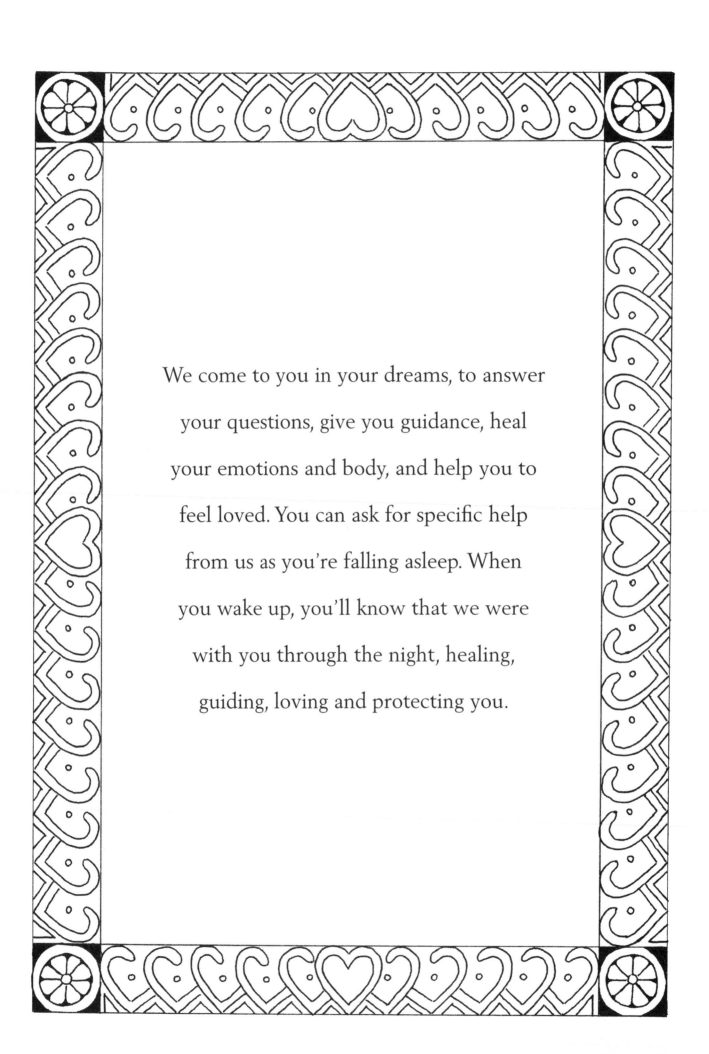

We come to you in your dreams, to answer your questions, give you guidance, heal your emotions and body, and help you to feel loved. You can ask for specific help from us as you're falling asleep. When you wake up, you'll know that we were with you through the night, healing, guiding, loving and protecting you.

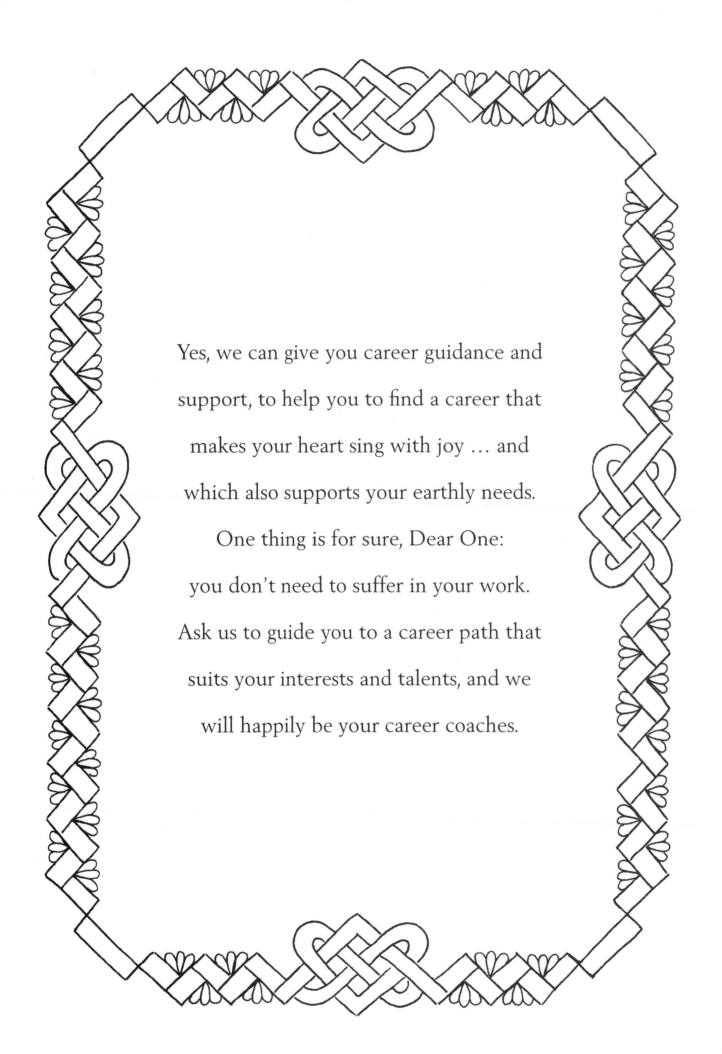

Yes, we can give you career guidance and
support, to help you to find a career that
makes your heart sing with joy … and
which also supports your earthly needs.
One thing is for sure, Dear One:
you don't need to suffer in your work.
Ask us to guide you to a career path that
suits your interests and talents, and we
will happily be your career coaches.

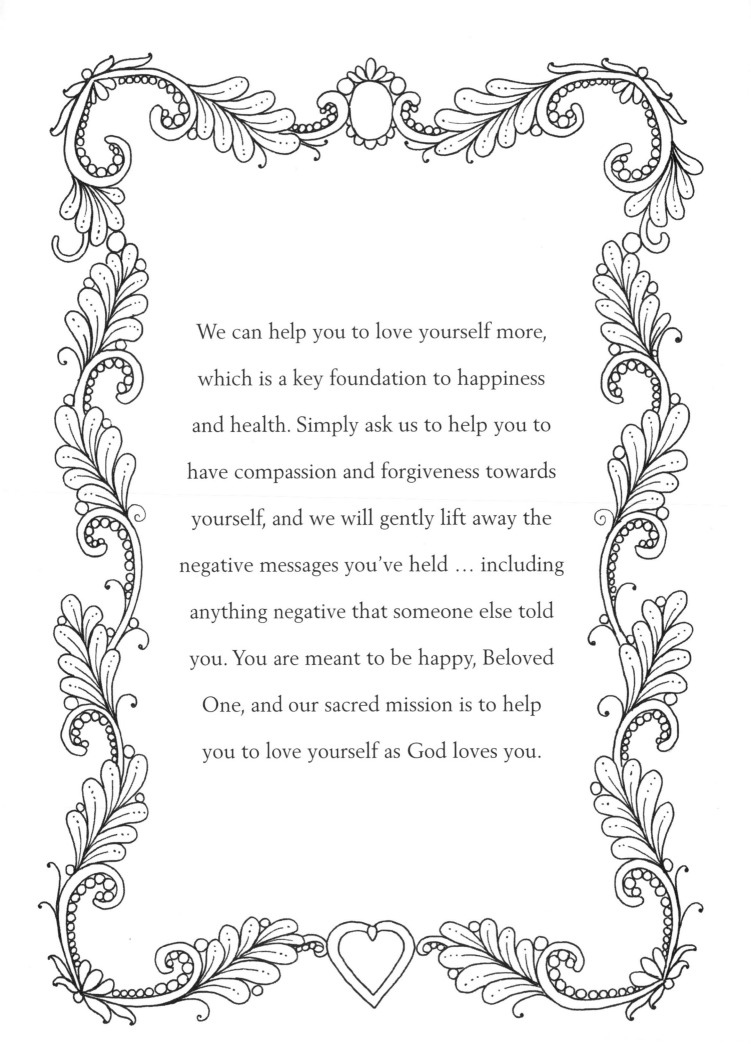

We can help you to love yourself more, which is a key foundation to happiness and health. Simply ask us to help you to have compassion and forgiveness towards yourself, and we will gently lift away the negative messages you've held … including anything negative that someone else told you. You are meant to be happy, Beloved One, and our sacred mission is to help you to love yourself as God loves you.

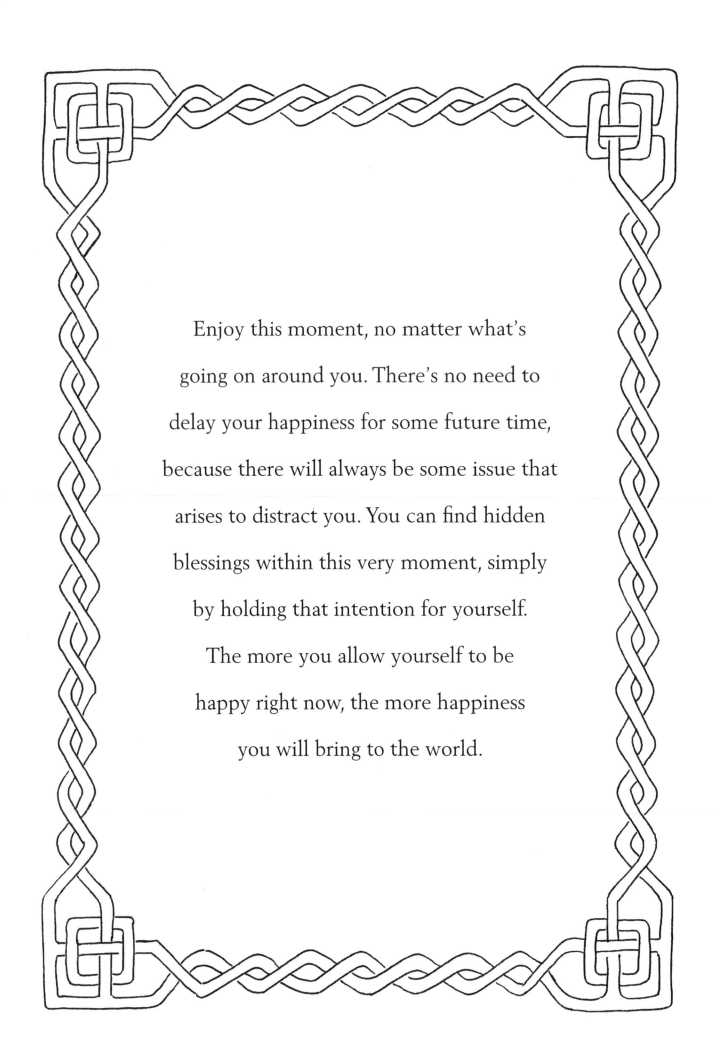

Enjoy this moment, no matter what's
going on around you. There's no need to
delay your happiness for some future time,
because there will always be some issue that
arises to distract you. You can find hidden
blessings within this very moment, simply
by holding that intention for yourself.
The more you allow yourself to be
happy right now, the more happiness
you will bring to the world.

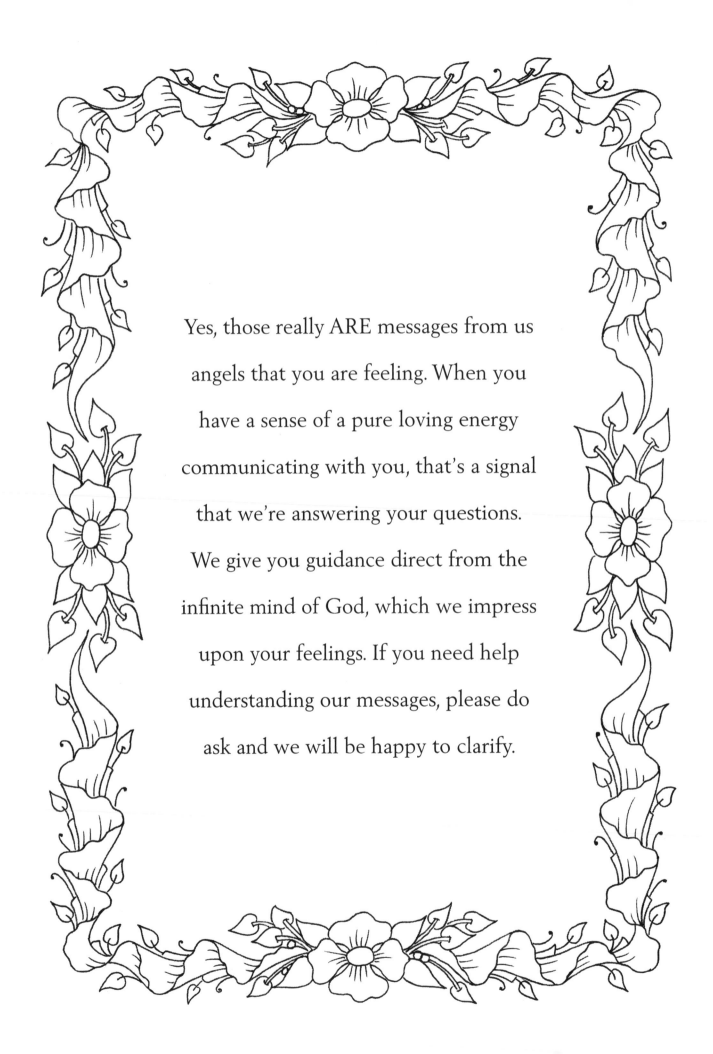

Yes, those really ARE messages from us angels that you are feeling. When you have a sense of a pure loving energy communicating with you, that's a signal that we're answering your questions. We give you guidance direct from the infinite mind of God, which we impress upon your feelings. If you need help understanding our messages, please do ask and we will be happy to clarify.

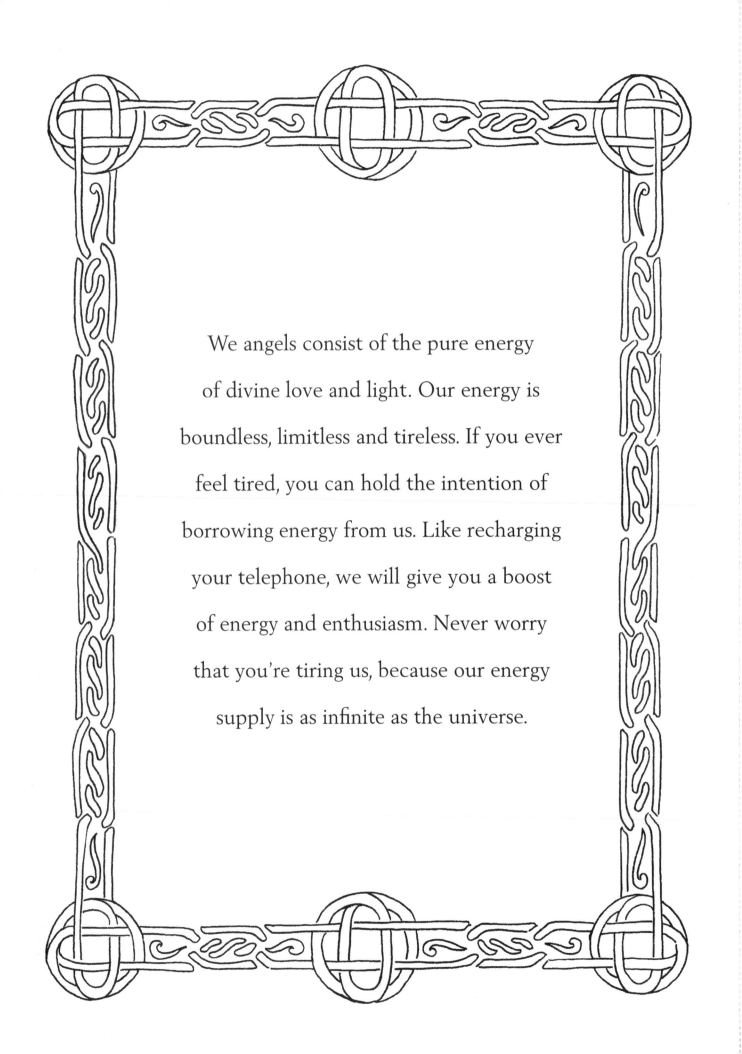

We angels consist of the pure energy
of divine love and light. Our energy is
boundless, limitless and tireless. If you ever
feel tired, you can hold the intention of
borrowing energy from us. Like recharging
your telephone, we will give you a boost
of energy and enthusiasm. Never worry
that you're tiring us, because our energy
supply is as infinite as the universe.

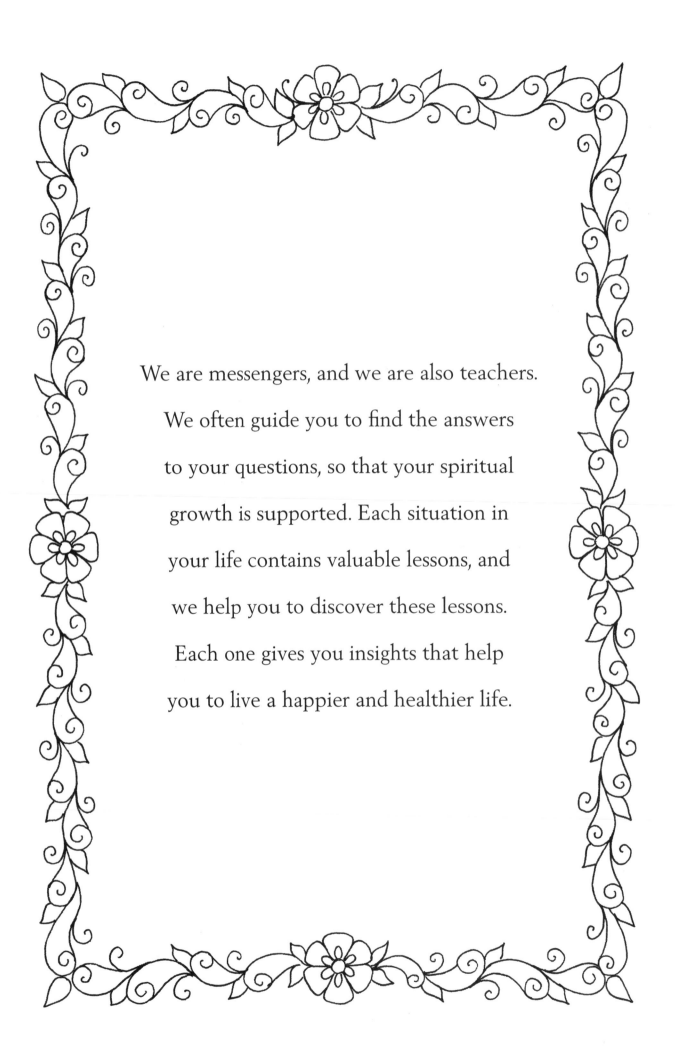

We are messengers, and we are also teachers.

We often guide you to find the answers

to your questions, so that your spiritual

growth is supported. Each situation in

your life contains valuable lessons, and

we help you to discover these lessons.

Each one gives you insights that help

you to live a happier and healthier life.

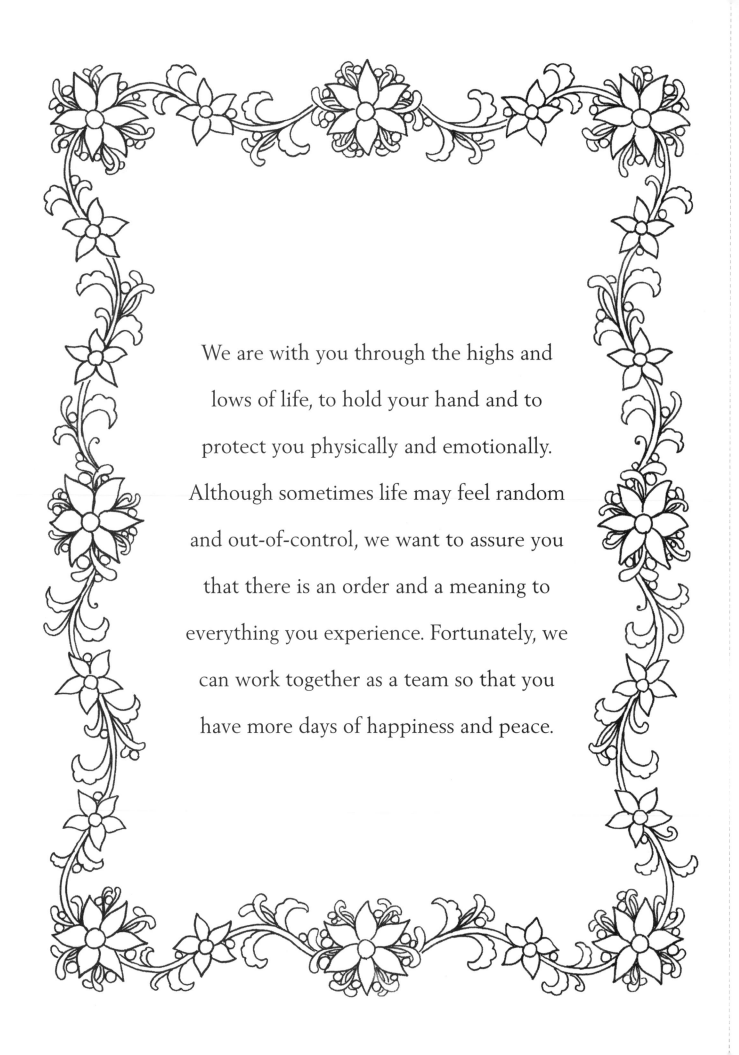

We are with you through the highs and
lows of life, to hold your hand and to
protect you physically and emotionally.
Although sometimes life may feel random
and out-of-control, we want to assure you
that there is an order and a meaning to
everything you experience. Fortunately, we
can work together as a team so that you
have more days of happiness and peace.

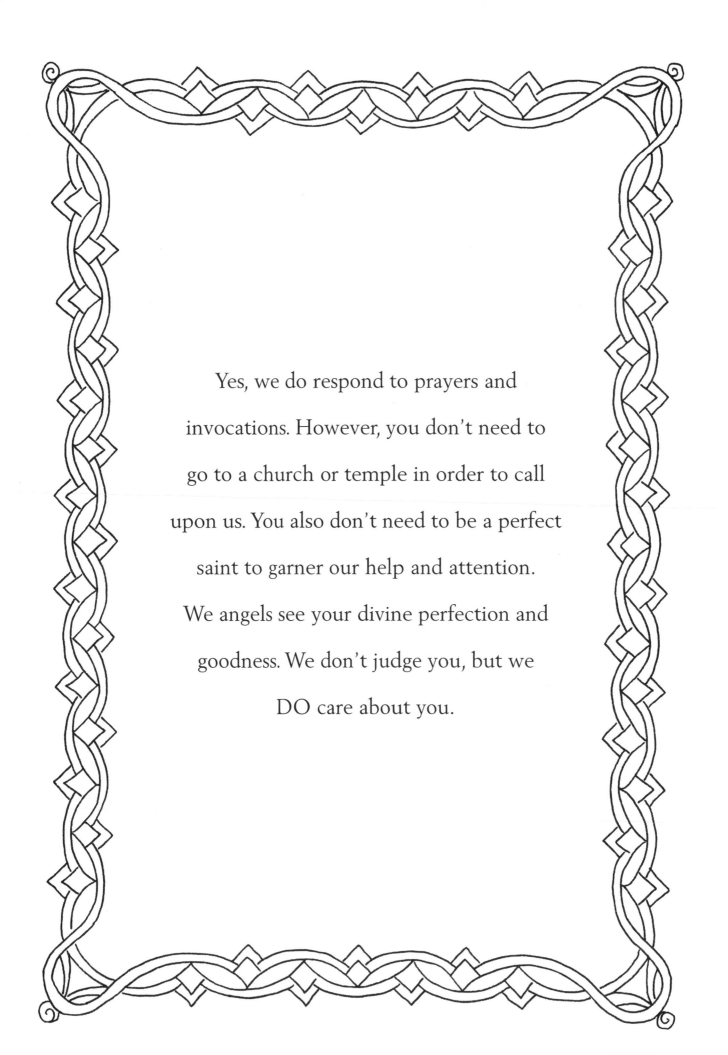

Yes, we do respond to prayers and invocations. However, you don't need to go to a church or temple in order to call upon us. You also don't need to be a perfect saint to garner our help and attention. We angels see your divine perfection and goodness. We don't judge you, but we DO care about you.

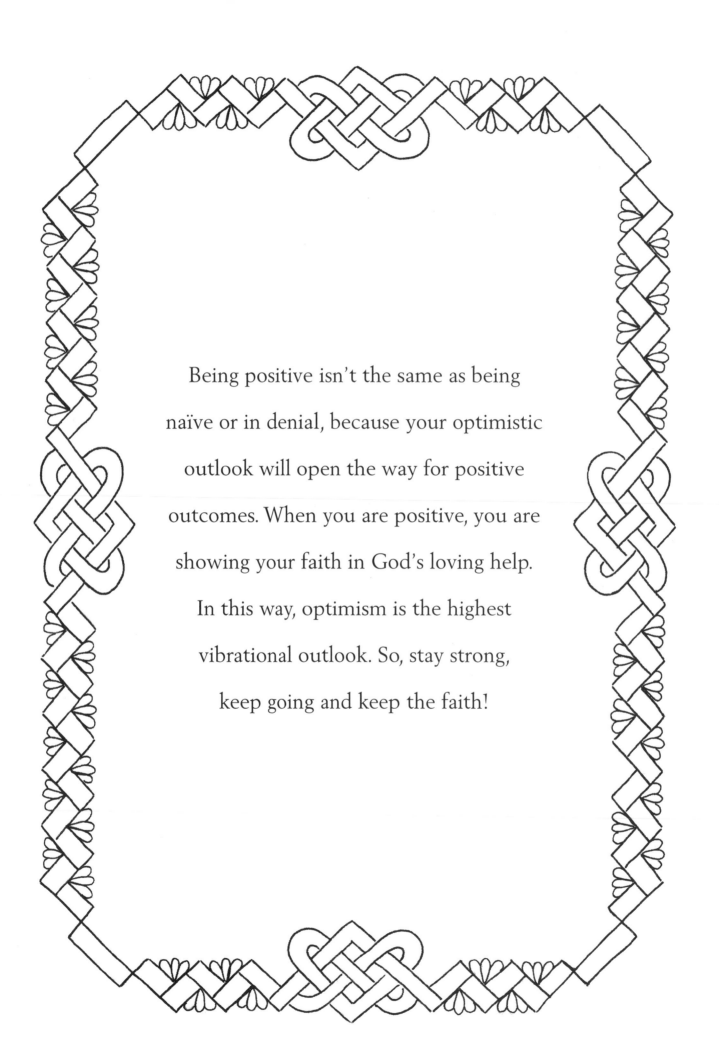

Being positive isn't the same as being

naïve or in denial, because your optimistic

outlook will open the way for positive

outcomes. When you are positive, you are

showing your faith in God's loving help.

In this way, optimism is the highest

vibrational outlook. So, stay strong,

keep going and keep the faith!

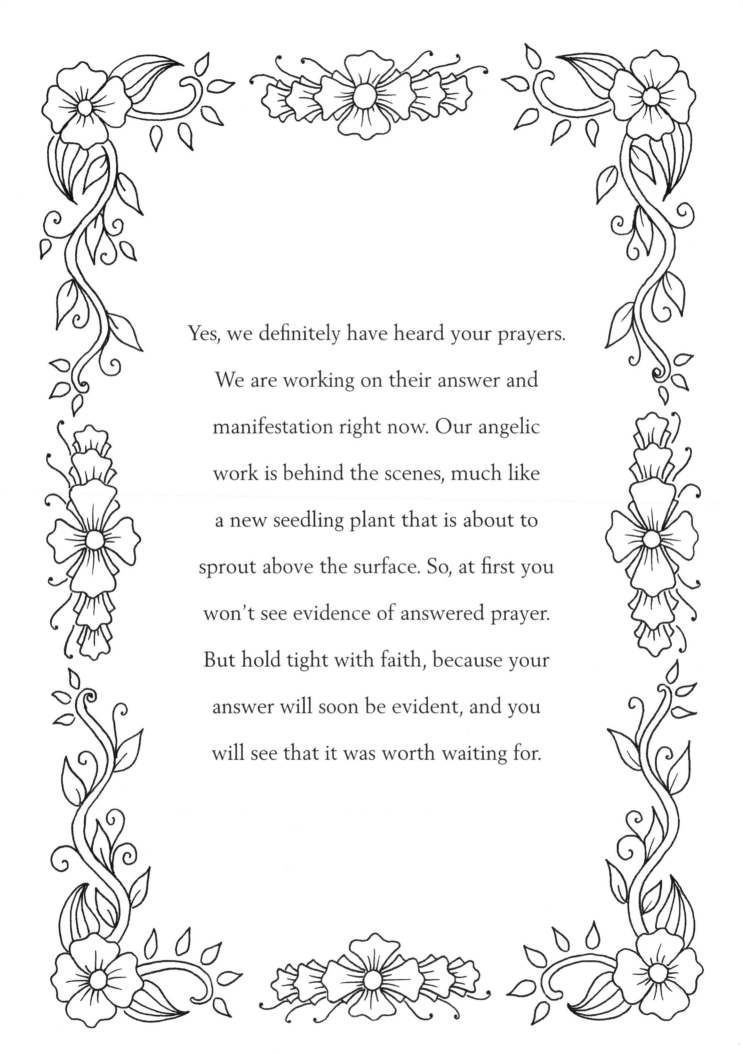

Yes, we definitely have heard your prayers.
We are working on their answer and
manifestation right now. Our angelic
work is behind the scenes, much like
a new seedling plant that is about to
sprout above the surface. So, at first you
won't see evidence of answered prayer.
But hold tight with faith, because your
answer will soon be evident, and you
will see that it was worth waiting for.

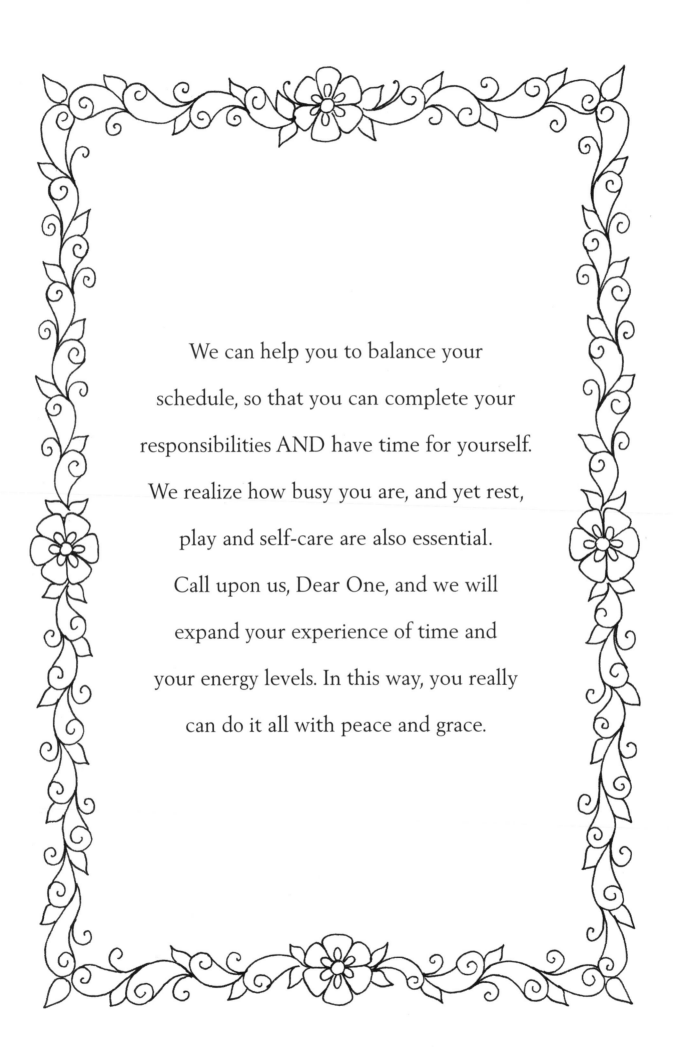

We can help you to balance your

schedule, so that you can complete your

responsibilities AND have time for yourself.

We realize how busy you are, and yet rest,

play and self-care are also essential.

Call upon us, Dear One, and we will

expand your experience of time and

your energy levels. In this way, you really

can do it all with peace and grace.

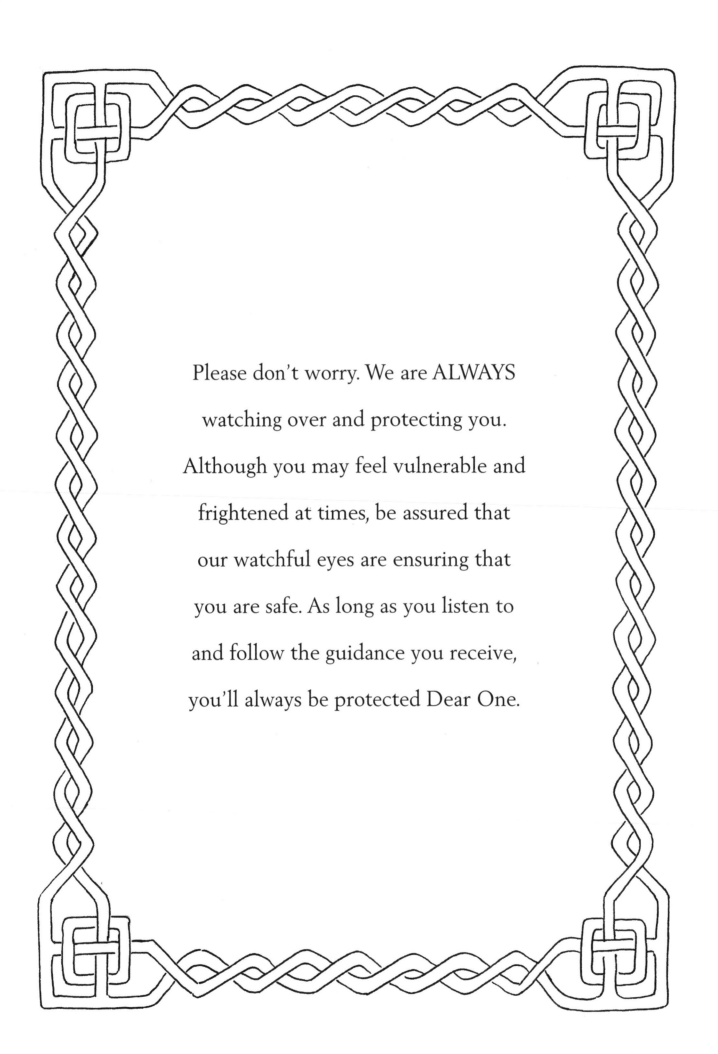

Please don't worry. We are ALWAYS

watching over and protecting you.

Although you may feel vulnerable and

frightened at times, be assured that

our watchful eyes are ensuring that

you are safe. As long as you listen to

and follow the guidance you receive,

you'll always be protected Dear One.

If you ever feel guilty about something,
please pray for help in sorting through
these feelings and thoughts. There's no
point in berating yourself, as this won't
help anything. What DOES help, though,
is learning and growing from the situation.
Make amends where needed, and then let
it go with full forgiveness for yourself.

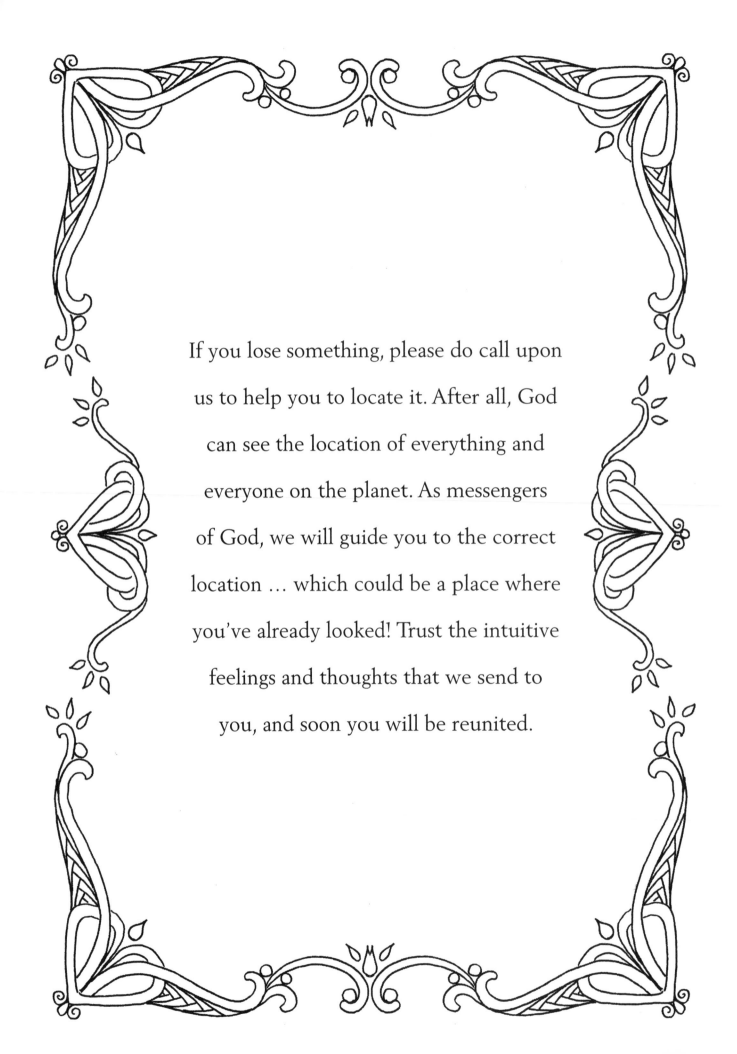

If you lose something, please do call upon us to help you to locate it. After all, God can see the location of everything and everyone on the planet. As messengers of God, we will guide you to the correct location … which could be a place where you've already looked! Trust the intuitive feelings and thoughts that we send to you, and soon you will be reunited.

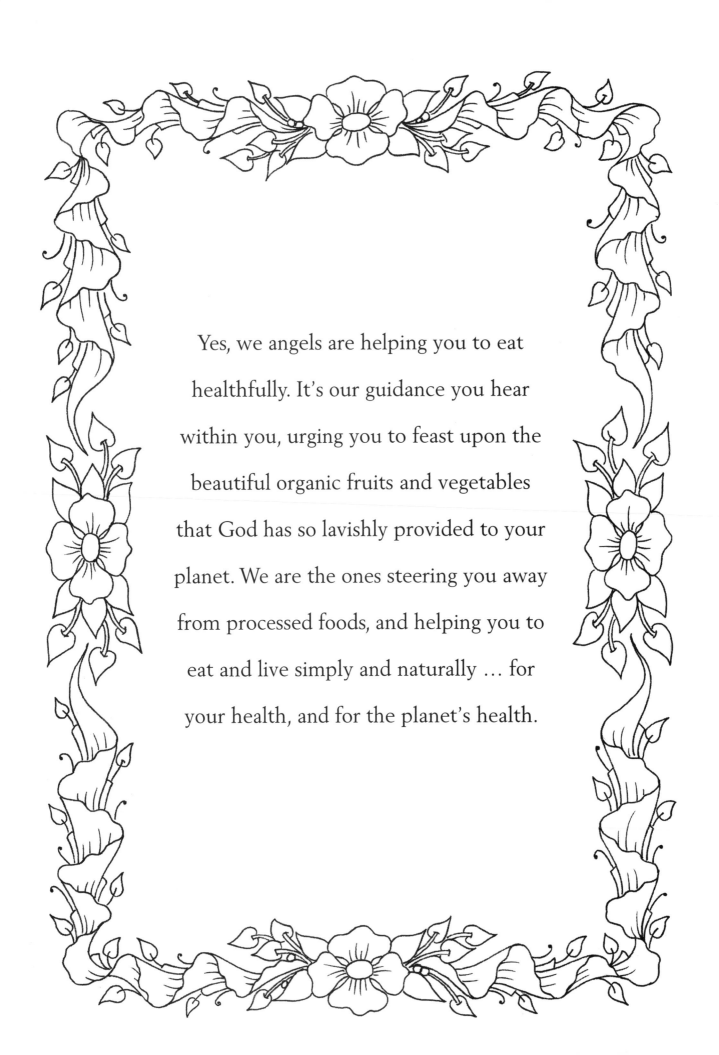

Yes, we angels are helping you to eat
healthfully. It's our guidance you hear
within you, urging you to feast upon the
beautiful organic fruits and vegetables
that God has so lavishly provided to your
planet. We are the ones steering you away
from processed foods, and helping you to
eat and live simply and naturally … for
your health, and for the planet's health.

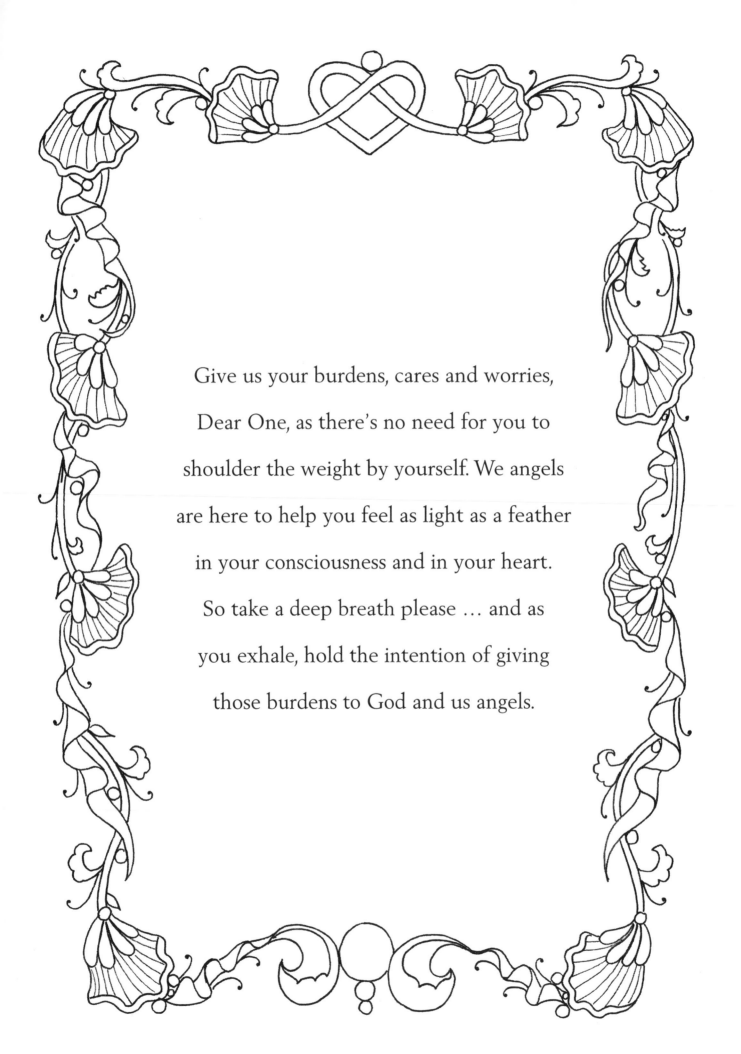

Give us your burdens, cares and worries,

Dear One, as there's no need for you to

shoulder the weight by yourself. We angels

are here to help you feel as light as a feather

in your consciousness and in your heart.

So take a deep breath please … and as

you exhale, hold the intention of giving

those burdens to God and us angels.

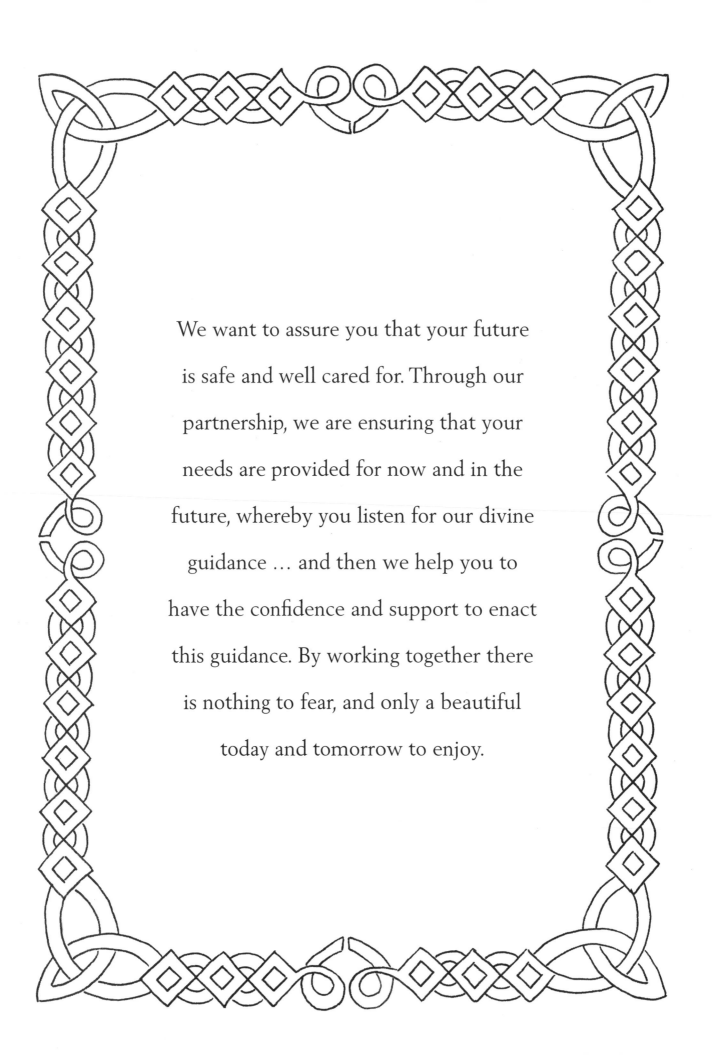

We want to assure you that your future is safe and well cared for. Through our partnership, we are ensuring that your needs are provided for now and in the future, whereby you listen for our divine guidance … and then we help you to have the confidence and support to enact this guidance. By working together there is nothing to fear, and only a beautiful today and tomorrow to enjoy.

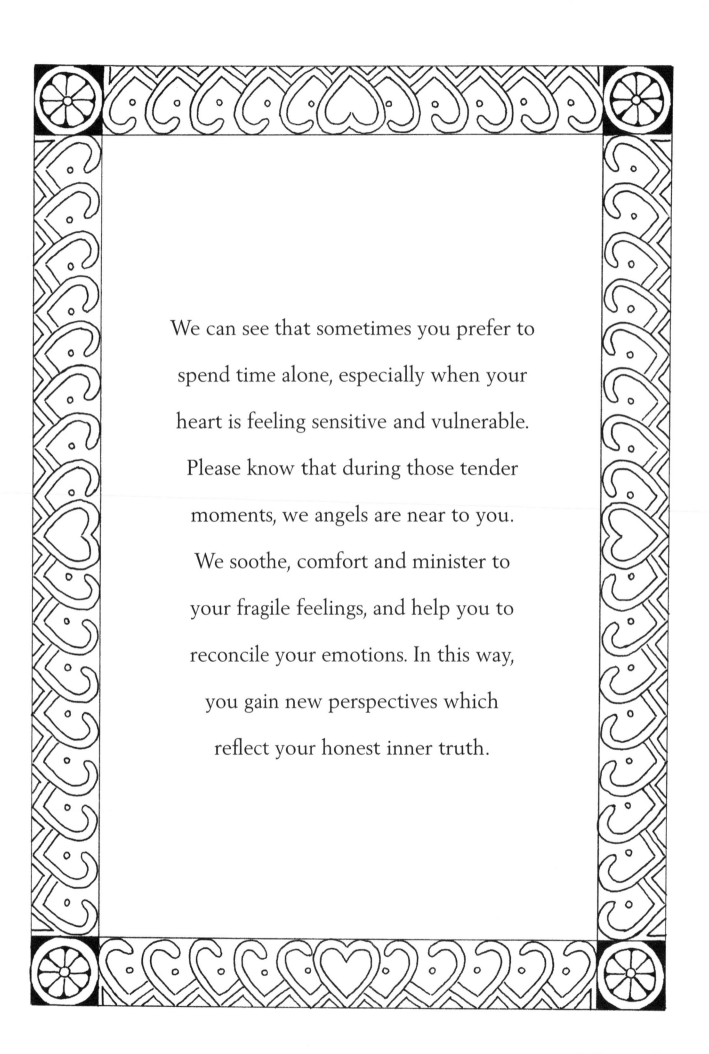

We can see that sometimes you prefer to

spend time alone, especially when your

heart is feeling sensitive and vulnerable.

Please know that during those tender

moments, we angels are near to you.

We soothe, comfort and minister to

your fragile feelings, and help you to

reconcile your emotions. In this way,

you gain new perspectives which

reflect your honest inner truth.

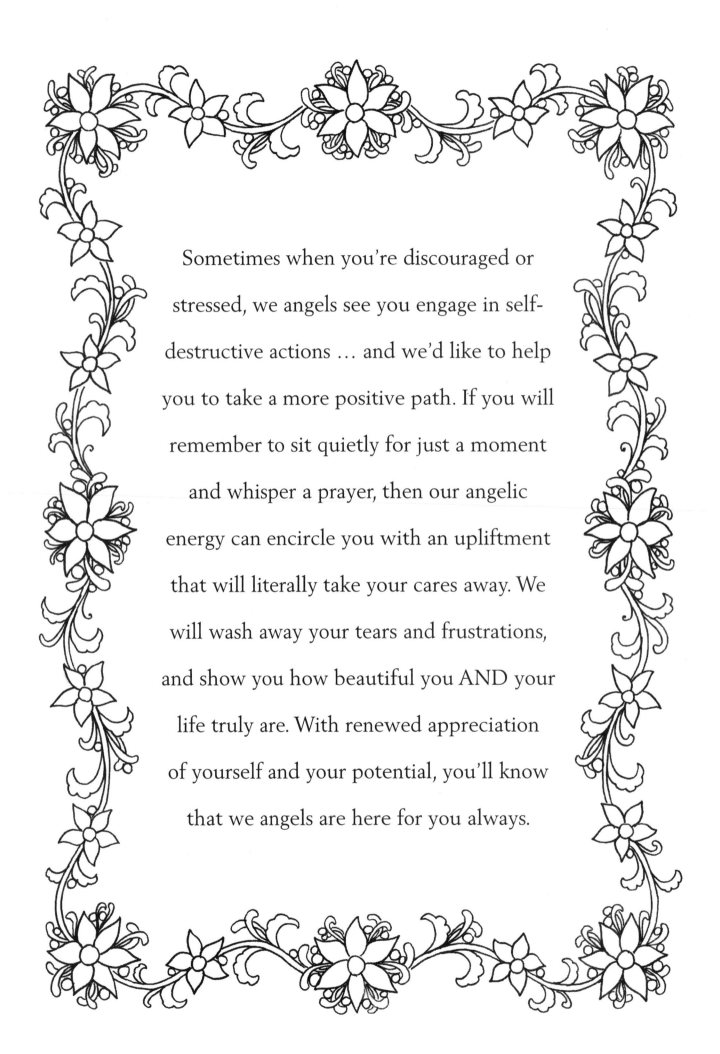

Sometimes when you're discouraged or stressed, we angels see you engage in self-destructive actions … and we'd like to help you to take a more positive path. If you will remember to sit quietly for just a moment and whisper a prayer, then our angelic energy can encircle you with an upliftment that will literally take your cares away. We will wash away your tears and frustrations, and show you how beautiful you AND your life truly are. With renewed appreciation of yourself and your potential, you'll know that we angels are here for you always.

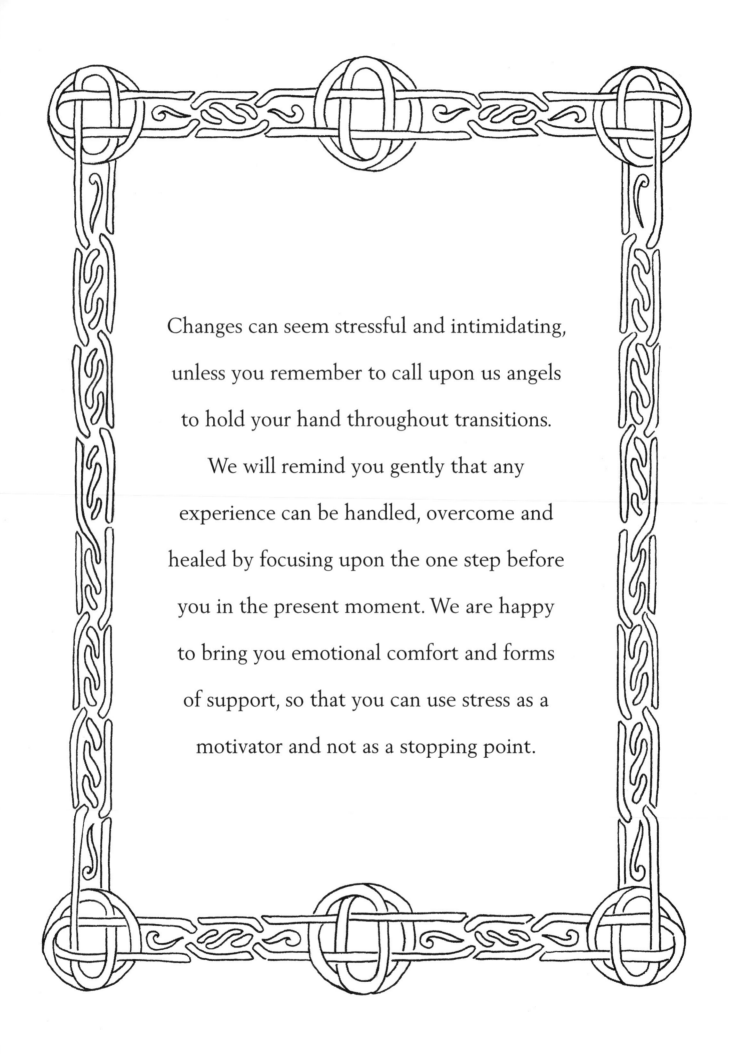

Changes can seem stressful and intimidating,

unless you remember to call upon us angels

to hold your hand throughout transitions.

We will remind you gently that any

experience can be handled, overcome and

healed by focusing upon the one step before

you in the present moment. We are happy

to bring you emotional comfort and forms

of support, so that you can use stress as a

motivator and not as a stopping point.

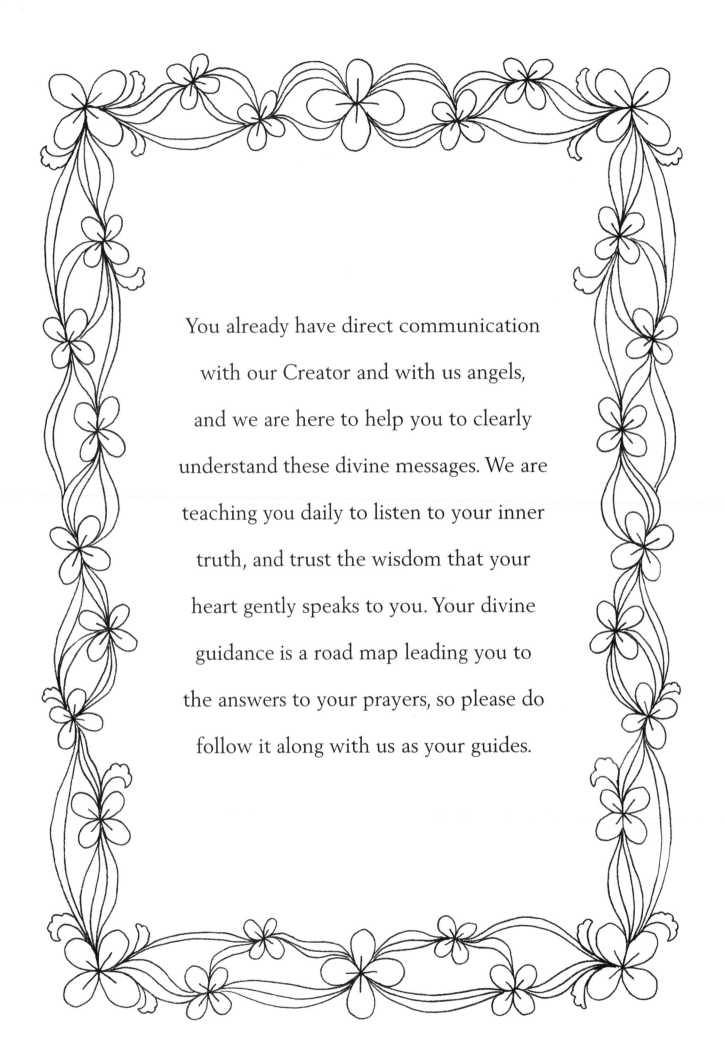

You already have direct communication with our Creator and with us angels, and we are here to help you to clearly understand these divine messages. We are teaching you daily to listen to your inner truth, and trust the wisdom that your heart gently speaks to you. Your divine guidance is a road map leading you to the answers to your prayers, so please do follow it along with us as your guides.

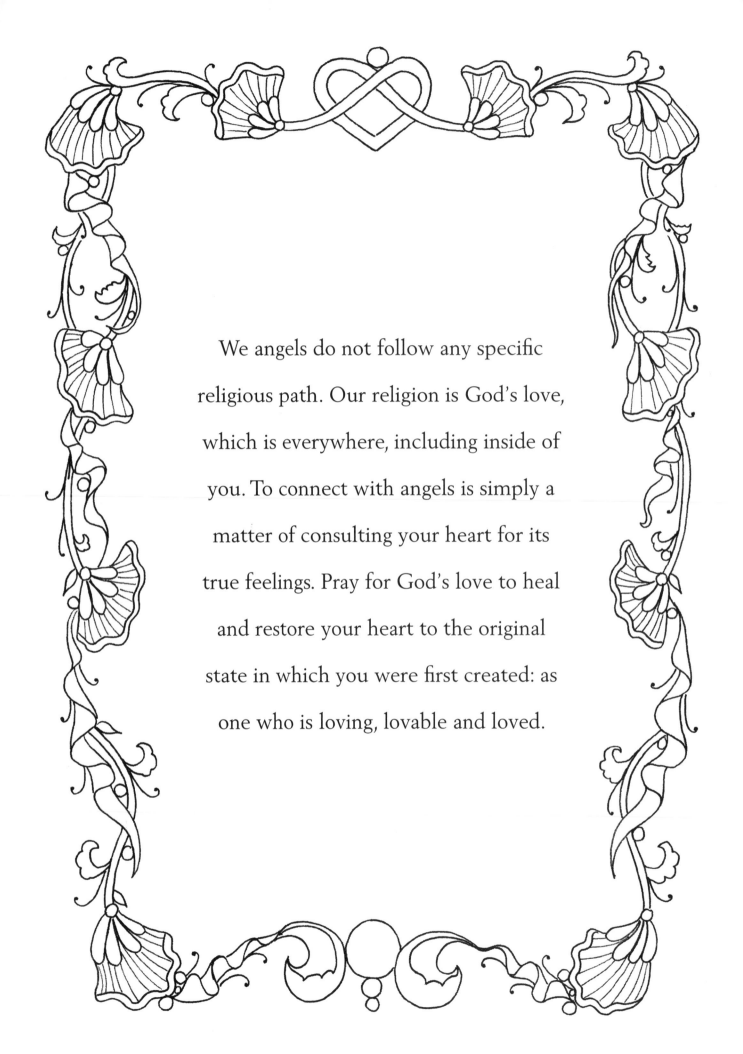

We angels do not follow any specific religious path. Our religion is God's love, which is everywhere, including inside of you. To connect with angels is simply a matter of consulting your heart for its true feelings. Pray for God's love to heal and restore your heart to the original state in which you were first created: as one who is loving, lovable and loved.

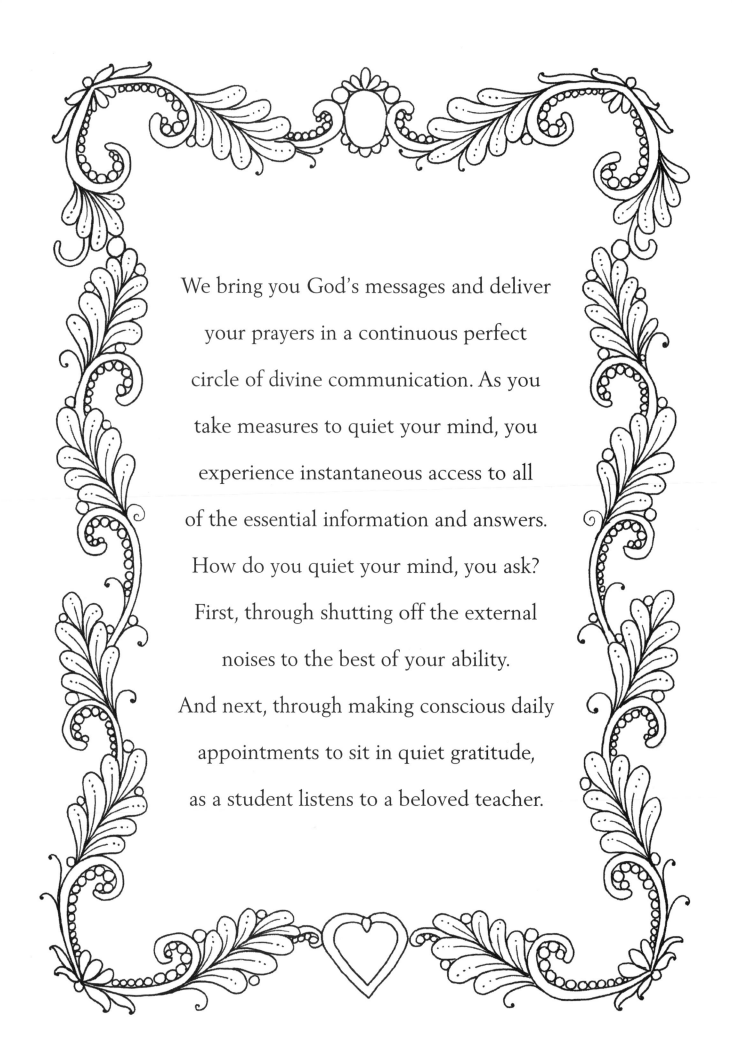

We bring you God's messages and deliver
your prayers in a continuous perfect
circle of divine communication. As you
take measures to quiet your mind, you
experience instantaneous access to all
of the essential information and answers.
How do you quiet your mind, you ask?
First, through shutting off the external
noises to the best of your ability.
And next, through making conscious daily
appointments to sit in quiet gratitude,
as a student listens to a beloved teacher.

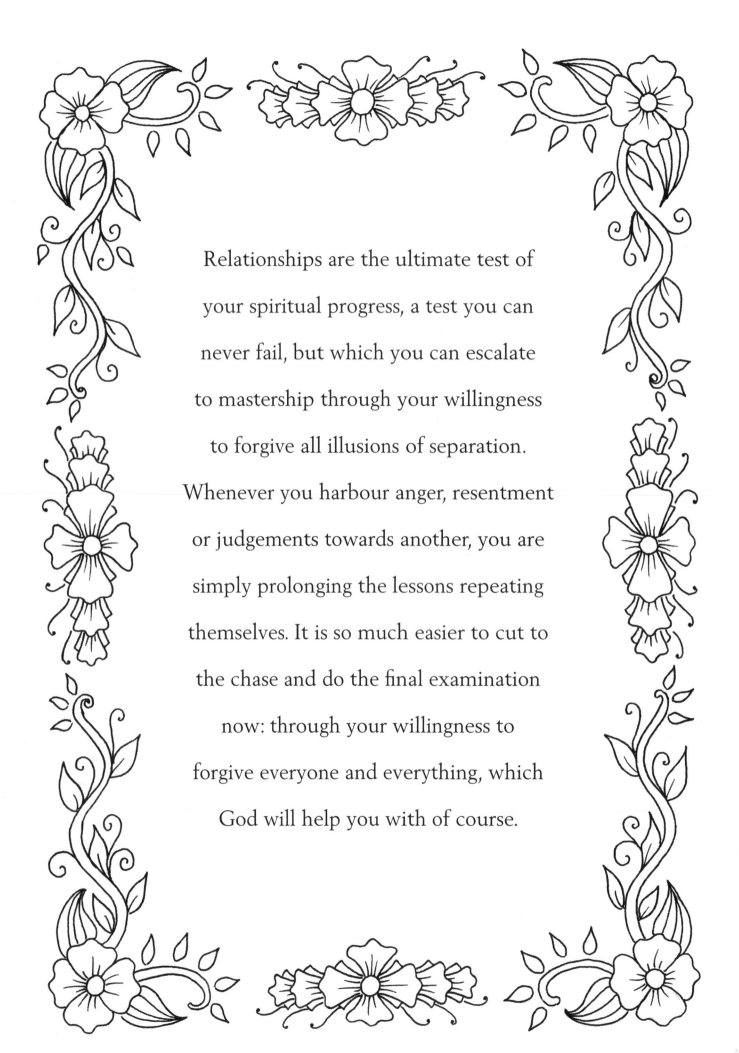

Relationships are the ultimate test of your spiritual progress, a test you can never fail, but which you can escalate to mastership through your willingness to forgive all illusions of separation. Whenever you harbour anger, resentment or judgements towards another, you are simply prolonging the lessons repeating themselves. It is so much easier to cut to the chase and do the final examination now: through your willingness to forgive everyone and everything, which God will help you with of course.

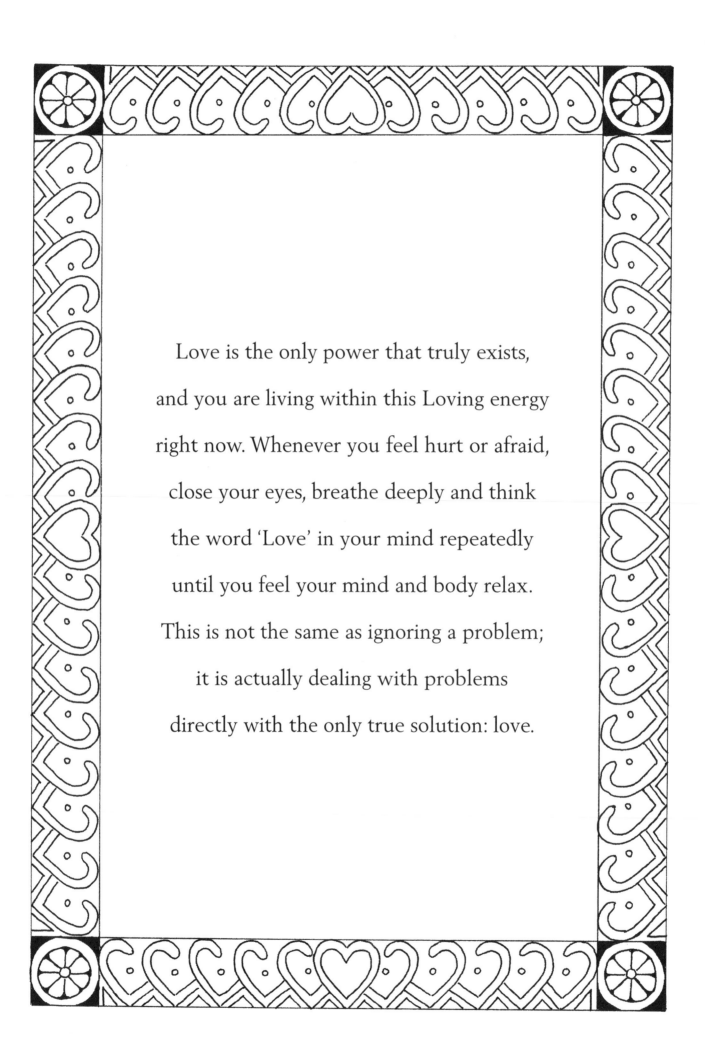

Love is the only power that truly exists,

and you are living within this Loving energy

right now. Whenever you feel hurt or afraid,

close your eyes, breathe deeply and think

the word 'Love' in your mind repeatedly

until you feel your mind and body relax.

This is not the same as ignoring a problem;

it is actually dealing with problems

directly with the only true solution: love.

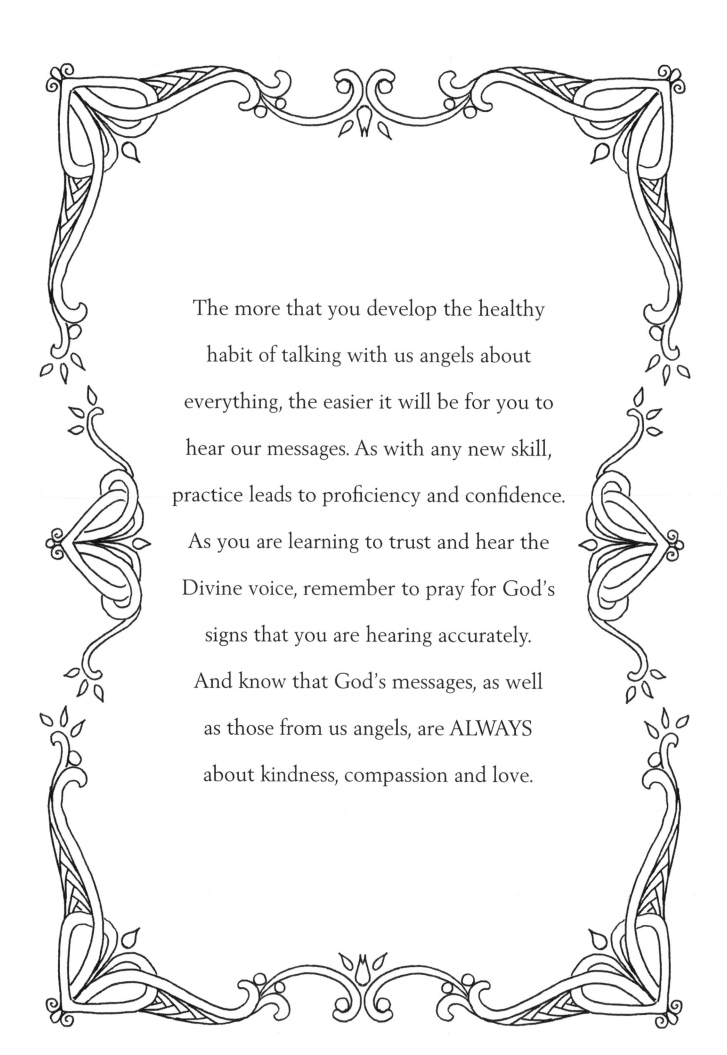

The more that you develop the healthy habit of talking with us angels about everything, the easier it will be for you to hear our messages. As with any new skill, practice leads to proficiency and confidence. As you are learning to trust and hear the Divine voice, remember to pray for God's signs that you are hearing accurately. And know that God's messages, as well as those from us angels, are ALWAYS about kindness, compassion and love.

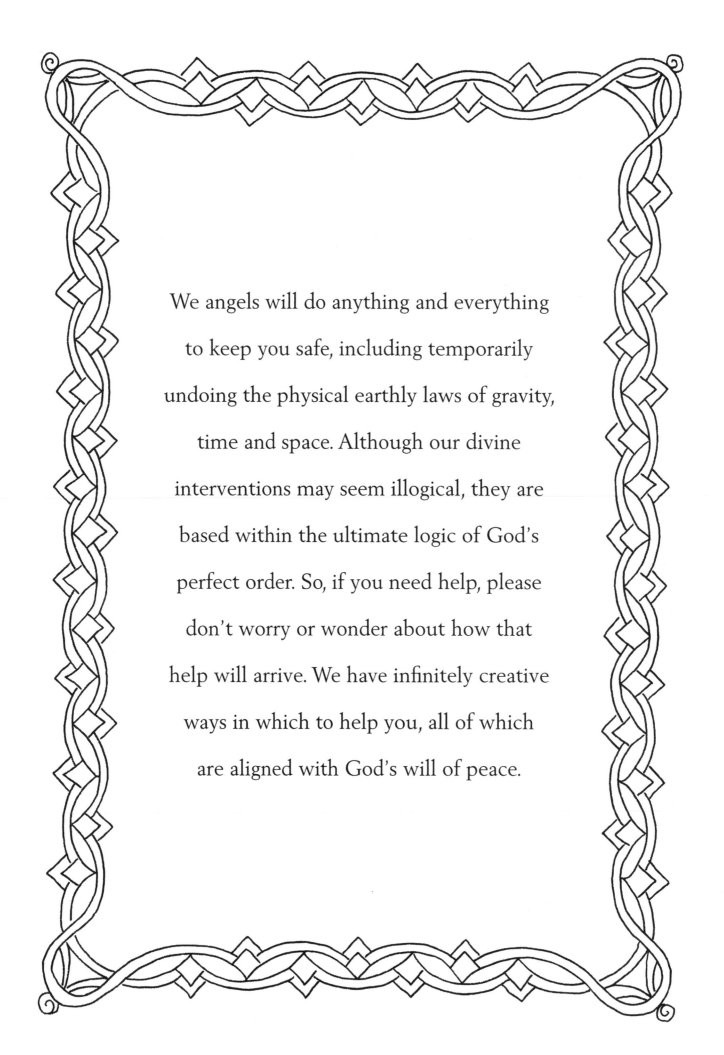

We angels will do anything and everything
to keep you safe, including temporarily
undoing the physical earthly laws of gravity,
time and space. Although our divine
interventions may seem illogical, they are
based within the ultimate logic of God's
perfect order. So, if you need help, please
don't worry or wonder about how that
help will arrive. We have infinitely creative
ways in which to help you, all of which
are aligned with God's will of peace.

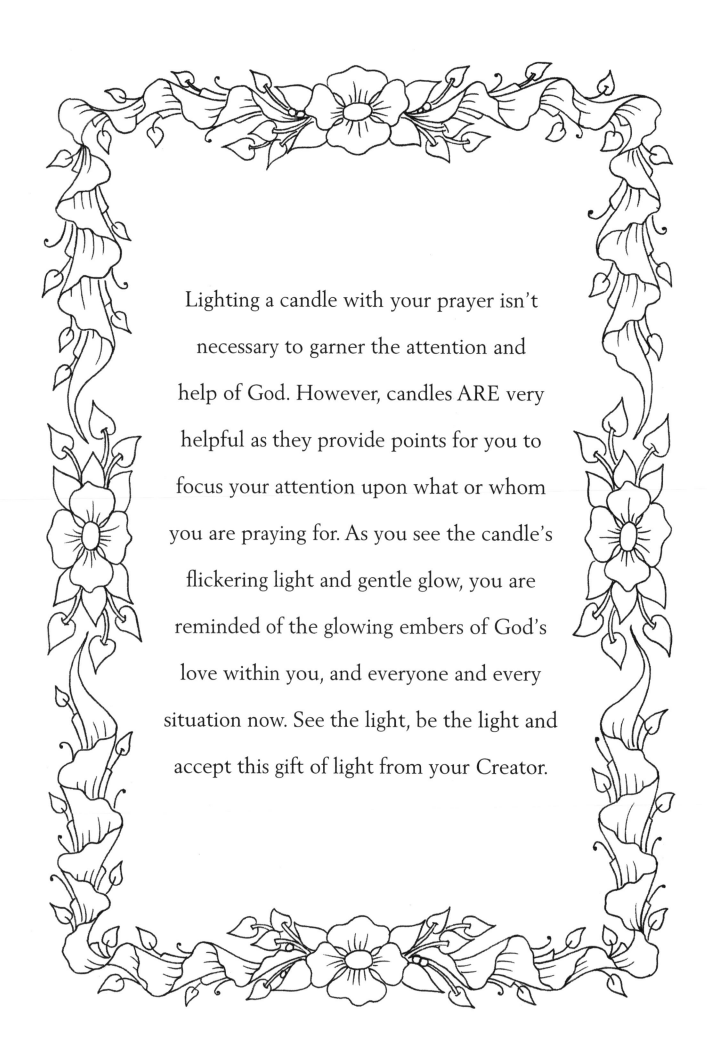

Lighting a candle with your prayer isn't necessary to garner the attention and help of God. However, candles ARE very helpful as they provide points for you to focus your attention upon what or whom you are praying for. As you see the candle's flickering light and gentle glow, you are reminded of the glowing embers of God's love within you, and everyone and every situation now. See the light, be the light and accept this gift of light from your Creator.

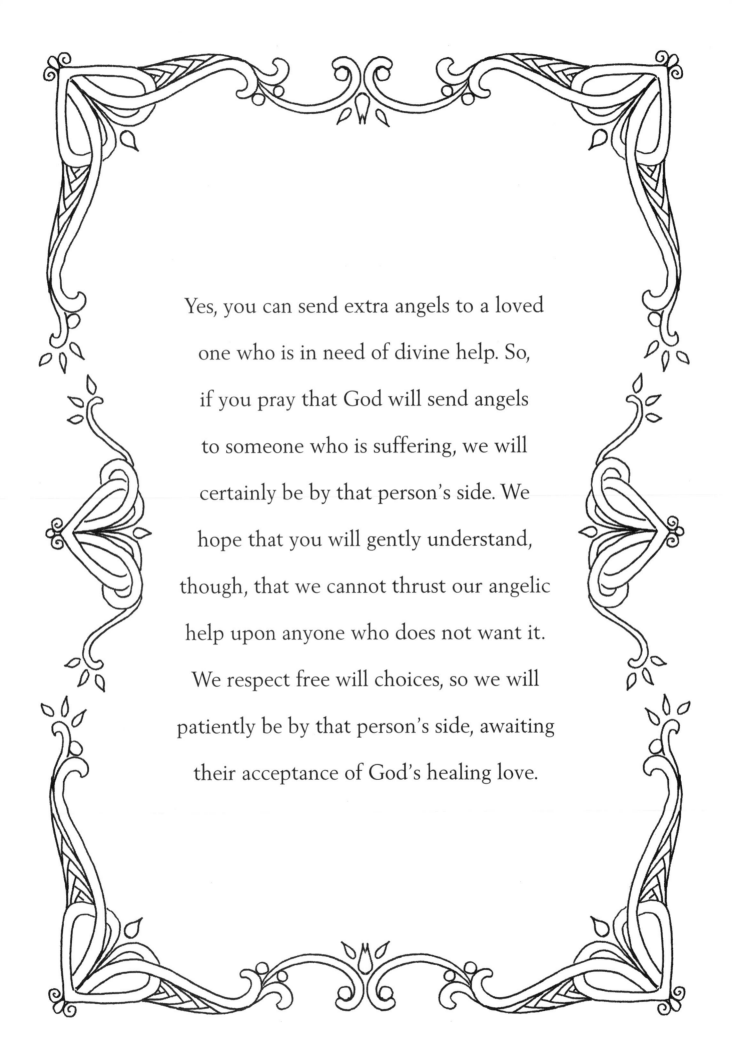

Yes, you can send extra angels to a loved

one who is in need of divine help. So,

if you pray that God will send angels

to someone who is suffering, we will

certainly be by that person's side. We

hope that you will gently understand,

though, that we cannot thrust our angelic

help upon anyone who does not want it.

We respect free will choices, so we will

patiently be by that person's side, awaiting

their acceptance of God's healing love.

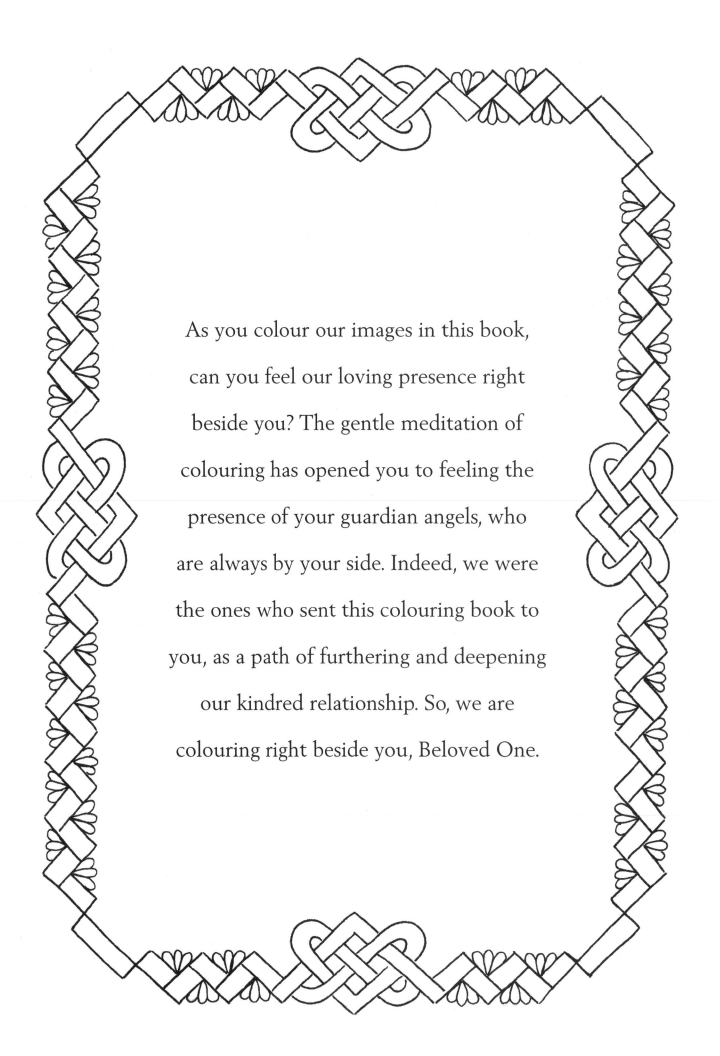

As you colour our images in this book,
can you feel our loving presence right
beside you? The gentle meditation of
colouring has opened you to feeling the
presence of your guardian angels, who
are always by your side. Indeed, we were
the ones who sent this colouring book to
you, as a path of furthering and deepening
our kindred relationship. So, we are
colouring right beside you, Beloved One.

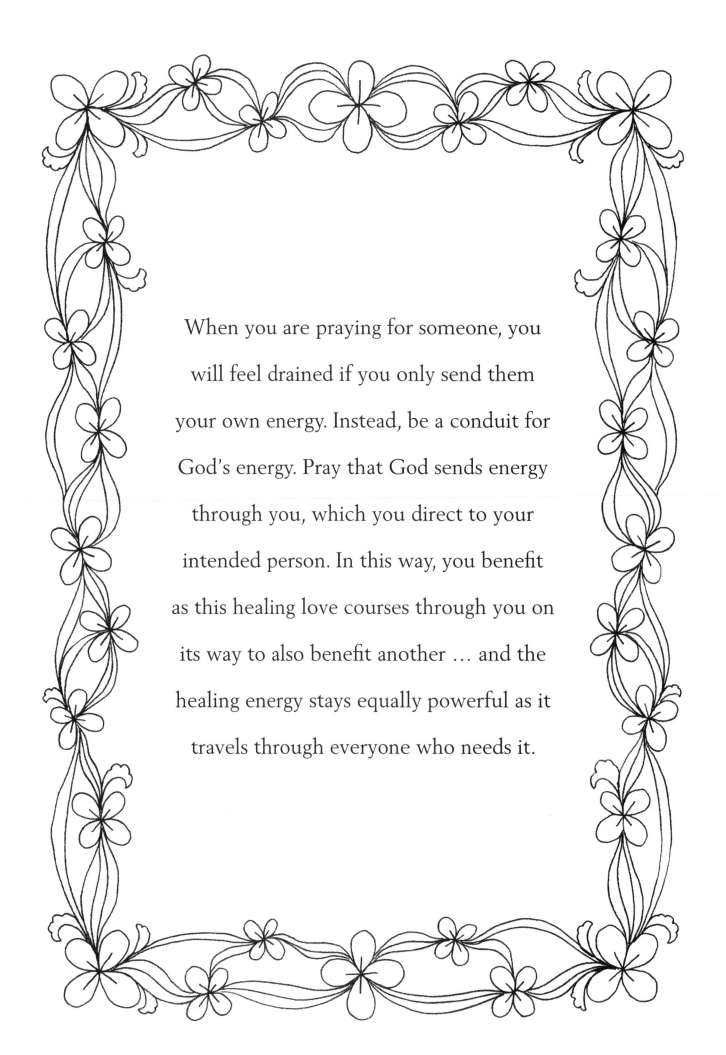

When you are praying for someone, you will feel drained if you only send them your own energy. Instead, be a conduit for God's energy. Pray that God sends energy through you, which you direct to your intended person. In this way, you benefit as this healing love courses through you on its way to also benefit another … and the healing energy stays equally powerful as it travels through everyone who needs it.

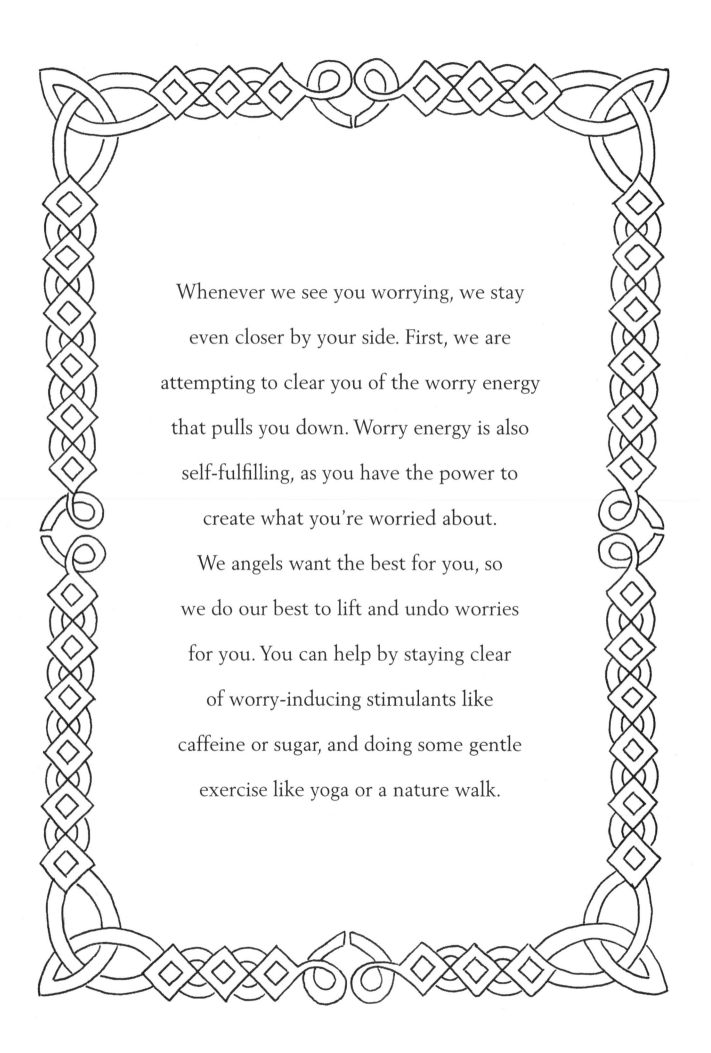

Whenever we see you worrying, we stay

even closer by your side. First, we are

attempting to clear you of the worry energy

that pulls you down. Worry energy is also

self-fulfilling, as you have the power to

create what you're worried about.

We angels want the best for you, so

we do our best to lift and undo worries

for you. You can help by staying clear

of worry-inducing stimulants like

caffeine or sugar, and doing some gentle

exercise like yoga or a nature walk.

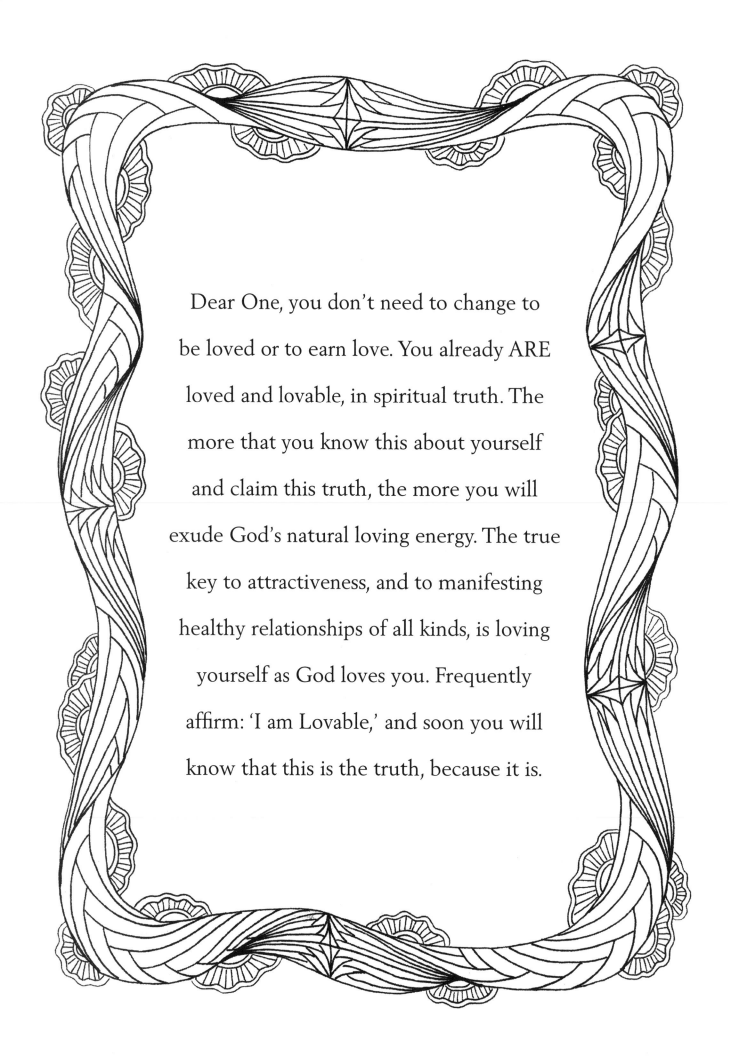

Dear One, you don't need to change to be loved or to earn love. You already ARE loved and lovable, in spiritual truth. The more that you know this about yourself and claim this truth, the more you will exude God's natural loving energy. The true key to attractiveness, and to manifesting healthy relationships of all kinds, is loving yourself as God loves you. Frequently affirm: 'I am Lovable,' and soon you will know that this is the truth, because it is.

Whenever you see the number 4, think of us angels, as 4 is a symbol that we send to you. The number 4 is a reminder that you are never alone, and that we angels are always by your side. Look for 4s everywhere you go, and you will see them. They are purposely put in your path, so that you'll always know you are watched over, guided and loved. Very loved!

About the Author

Doreen Virtue holds BA, MA and PhD degrees in counselling psychology. She's the author of more than 50 books and oracle card decks dealing with spiritual topics. Best known for her work with the angels, Doreen is frequently called 'The Angel Lady'.

A lifelong activist and a vegan since 1996, Doreen is involved in charities and movements that support a healthy environment, fair treatment of animals, clean air and water, and organic non-GMO food for all.

Doreen has appeared on *Oprah*, CNN and other television and radio programmes, and writes the weekly column 'My Guardian Angel' for *Woman's World* magazine. Her products are available in most languages worldwide, on Kindle and other eBook platforms and as iTunes apps. She also has a live weekly radio show on Hay House Radio.

www.angeltherapy.com

About the Illustrator

Norma J. Burnell, certified Zentangle® teacher, is an accomplished artist and has been involved in the arts all of her life. She is a contributing author to *The Art of Zentangle* and to *The Art of Fashion Tangling*.

After discovering the art of Zentangle, Norma began incorporating 'tangles' into her own fantasy art and Fairy-Tangles™ was born. Many of her Fairy-Tangles drawings are now sold as rubber stamps for card making and other crafts, and her originals have been sold to collectors around the world.

Norma currently works for a small company creating websites and graphic design. She also teaches various art classes and continues to develop her own art. Her lifelong dream is to continue being an artist and to share her art with others.

www.fairy-tangles.com

HAY HOUSE COLOURING BOOKS

9781781807460
£9.99

'Take the time to create and play – it will bring you healing and create new possibilities for you.'

LOUISE HAY

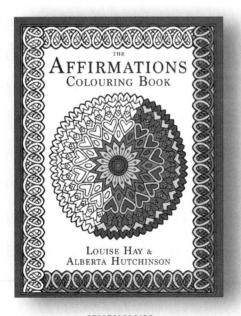

9781781806456
£9.99

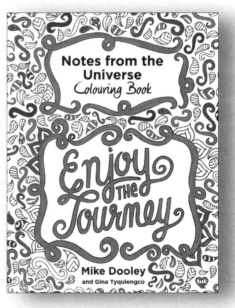

9781781806463
£9.99